The Pocket Encyclopedia of Spaceflight in Color

FRONTIERS OF SPACE

The Pocket Encyclopedia of
Spaceflight in Color

FRONTIERS OF SPACE

by
PHILIP BONO
FAAAS, AFAIAA, FBIS, MIAA
and
KENNETH GATLAND
FRAS, FBIS

Illustrated by

JOHN W. WOOD

TONY MITCHELL
NORMAN DINNAGE
WILLIAM HOBSON
JACK PELLING
BRIAN HILEY

THE MACMILLAN COMPANY

First American Edition 1969

First published in Great Britain in 1969 by Blandford Press Ltd, London

Library of Congress catalog card number: 74-83395

Printed and bound in Great Britain

ACKNOWLEDGEMENTS

The publishers and authors are particularly grateful to McDonnell-Douglas Corporation for providing a large number of outstanding illustrations. Permission to adapt various portions of company-sponsored studies also is gratefully acknowledged. Many references to these studies will be found throughout the text, particularly in Chapters Four to Eight. It is a pleasure to record special appreciation and recognition of the following individuals from McDonnell-Douglas Astronautics Co., whose published articles were freely consulted: J. C. Brizendine, A. B. Croshere, R. L. Gervais, R. D. Heitchue, R. L. Johnson, V. D. Kirkland, and F. C. Runge.

Special acknowledgement is also due to the National Aeronautics and Space Administration. A unique feature of this book is the remarkable colour photographs of the Earth and the Moon taken from Gemini and Apollo spacecraft. These have been supplied by Richard Friedman of NASA's Office of the Assistant Administrator for International Affairs and his co-operation is gratefully acknowledged. The infra-red aerial photograph on page 20 is by courtesy of the University of Maine. For material relating to the Saturn 1 orbital workshop we are indebted to Foster Haley of NASA's George C. Marshall Space Flight Center.

Photographs and technical data have also been supplied by the Boeing Company; North American Rockwell and McDonnell-Douglas Corporation (Saturn 5); Grumman Aircraft Engineering Corporation (Apollo lunar module; Northrop Corporation (M-2/F-2 and HL-10 lifting bodies); Martin Marietta Corporation (X-24A lifting-body); Lockheed-California Company (lifting-body concepts); British Aircraft Corporation (MUSTARD project); ERNO (air-breathing booster concept), and TRW Systems Group and General Electric Company of the USA (Earth resources survey satellites). Iris Smith of the Novosti Press Agency in London kindly provided illustrations of Soviet Cosmos and Soyuz spacecraft upon which colour reproductions are based. The roll-out of Saturn 5 at the Kennedy Space Center (page 40) is from a photograph kindly supplied by W. A. ('Bill') Dunn of the United States Information Service in London.

Historical material relating to the Sänger Bredt antipodal bomber and the Boeing X-20 Dyna-Soar is from *Astronautics in the Sixties* by K. W. Gatland (Iliffe Books Ltd.)

The following additional sources have been freely consulted: *Spaceflight* (a monthly publication of the British Interplanetary Society), *Aviation Week and Space Technology*, and *Aerospace Technology*. The diagram on page 110 was originally compiled on behalf of the BIS by Brian Buss of Hawker Siddeley Dynamics. The diagram on page 96 is based on an illustration which originally appeared in a Douglas engineering paper.

Many colour illustrations in this book have been specially prepared by artist John Wood and his associates, Tony Mitchell, Bill Hobson, Brian Hiley and Jack Pelling. These specialists in the art of aerospace illustration are fast winning an international reputation. Mention must also be made of McDonnell-Douglas artists who worked alongside project engineers on the original design studies.

In large measure this book is an international venture. We are especially grateful to Camille Bono of Costa Mesa, California, and Doreen Gatland, of New Malden, Surrey, who gave valuable assistance in preparing the manuscript for publication though working more than 5,000 miles apart.

For the convenience of international editions the 80-page colour section is bound at the front of the book. Captions which appear on the colour pages are fully amplified in the text.

PHILIP BONO   KENNETH GATLAND
Costa Mesa California, USA   *New Malden, Surrey, England*

CONTENTS

INTRODUCTION

Now that man has reached the Moon bold new frontiers of space are about to open. The opportunities extend from Earth-orbiting space stations and scientific outposts on the Moon to flights to the nearer planets.

The activities are far from being abstract scientific pursuits. Increasingly, space exploration is being recognized as spearheading human progress in many directions. It is giving birth to thousands of new ideas, inventions, and technical innovations, many of which find practical application in everyday life. Our entire future, for example, will be dominated by computers and high-speed global telecommunications which the exacting demands of space research have encouraged and will continue to stimulate.

Space has become the 'forcing ground' for important new materials, electronics, computers, data processing, machine tools, automation, medical instrumentation, power sources, and very much more. It has led to more efficient management techniques now being applied to industry at large, and this alone represents a substantial profit from space investment.

The lessons of space are being learned rapidly by the under-developed countries who will be among the first to benefit. Ceylon's delegate expressed it well at the Vienna Conference on *Exploration and Peaceful Uses of Outer Space*:

> We are often asked [he said], why we show interest in space research when we have not yet solved the problems of poverty and illiteracy. Probably the answer is that we wish to solve them at a new level. It is one thing to eliminate illiteracy in the old-fashioned way, but quite another to do so by television and satellite re-transmission.

Brazil is preparing to beat illiteracy and raise economic standards by satellite techniques. India has her sights on combating the population explosion. The Indian population on 1 November

1968 was officially stated to be 528,437,800 with a monthly increase exceeding one million; 80 per cent of the people live in widely scattered rural communities. It is the aim to provide each of some 560,000 villages with at least one television set capable of receiving satellite-relayed programmes placing emphasis on family planning, hygiene, agriculture, and basic education. It could be the only way of preventing ultimate disaster.

As we proceed with new areas of satellite technology, opportunities for assisting developed and underdeveloped countries will grow. Some of the most exciting and rewarding avenues of space research in the next decades will be directed towards our own planet in such fields as direct-broadcasting educational television, advance weather forecasting, and Earth-resources survey. The last-mentioned – which receives great emphasis in this book – has wide economic importance. We are beginning to see how multi-spectral cameras can obtain rapid and accurate assessments of the world's agricultural resources, crop growth and health, and the density of human and animal populations. Patterns of sea life will be traced from orbit, and the land mass and continental shelves probed for minerals, oil, fresh water, and other vital natural resources. Manned orbital systems are bound to play an important role in exploiting these techniques.

We can already envisage the day when the world's 'knowledge explosion' is contained and controlled by computerized information banks which dispense their information via satellites to subscribers in all parts of the world. The enormous demands for data processing and rapid dissemination of results to all parts of the globe (required for the effective use of Earth resources satellite data) can transform our world's business efficiency and, incidentally, help create the environment for true international co-operation. Quite soon the need for an International Space Agency will arise to ensure that all nations, rich and poor, derive the maximum benefit from our space-conditioned future. Under United Nations' auspices, ideally, this would also ensure that future explorations beyond our planet are developed in partnership rather than wasteful competition.

Apart from observing the Earth, manned space stations can also become platforms for vastly extending the scope of optical and radio astronomy free from atmospheric interference or absorption. They can also provide an extension of Earth-based laboratories in many important areas of science and technology where full advantage can be taken of weightlessness, radiation across the entire spectrum, and vacuum conditions better than can be produced on Earth. In this grossly changed environment, classical problems in physics and chemistry can be re-studied, which can stimulate entirely new technologies. Advances are also probable in medicine and biology.

Any prophecy of benefits accruing to mankind over the next half-century of space technology is bound to invoke conjecture and speculation. To minimize the amount of crystal-gazing, most of the projections in this book are restricted to the period of the immediate future; i.e. up to the late 1980s. It is part of the argument that this future will be bound up with the development of some kind of re-usable launch vehicle.

In developing this particular thesis, engineering principles have been applied primarily to chemically propelled rockets. While every effort has been made to present engineering concepts in a form which can be readily grasped by the non-specialist with a technical curiosity, it is inevitable that some of the more unconventional features of recoverable boosters require fairly detailed explanation.

At the outset one must recognize that space travel is merely another form of transportation. In the past we have progressed from foot and animal travel to travel by ship, train, automobile and aircraft. Dr John Furbay, a philosopher of international repute, has gone so far as to suggest that only *three* major inventions have sprung from the creative genius of man. Each of these inventions was some kind of transportation device which stimulated human progress. The first allowed our ancestors to cast off the restrictions imposed by muscle-power as a means of propulsion. In all of prehistory, human endurance limited the extent of travel away from the caves which our ancestors inhabited 360,000 years ago. By harnessing the forces of nature to propel his first invention, man discovered that the wind-powered sailboat allowed him to exchange material goods with nearby tribes. Thus, by being able to communicate with perhaps 10 per cent of the existing world population, the beginning of civilized communities were evolved by early humans located in coastal settlements.

The next epoch-making invention, the wheel and later the paved road, broadened man's horizons to undreamed proportions when he learned that he could now travel distances of a few hundred miles. The settlers then were able to move far inland out of their coastal valleys, resulting in the eventual civilization of an additional 25 per cent of Earth's inhabitants.

Our third and most modern innovation, the aeroplane, gave man the ability to travel thousands of miles in a single day. By reaching previously inaccessible places, he was able to open up new territories and widen his experience still further. But, in large measure, his sphere of influence is still measured by the distance he can travel in a day before being overcome by the need to sleep.

In summary, man has already succeeded in exploiting the sea, the land and the air; progressively shrinking the size of his planet, until it can now be measured in several hours. What will be the effect on civilization of travelling by way of the only remaining medium – space – when dimensionally, in time, our Earth has been shrunk to less than one hour?

As we enter the age of the space rocket much remains to be done before it can take its place alongside more conventional means of transportation. The rocket boosters of today are not recovered for re-use; they are allowed to burn up while penetrating Earth's atmosphere or to splash wastefully into the sea. No other method of transportation could long survive the extravagance associated with disposal of the carrier vehicle *after only one use*. Truly efficient space exploration awaits the day when launching can be accomplished by a booster which can be recovered and re-used repeatedly.

To examine how the breakthrough can be achieved, Chapters Six and Seven of this book have adopted a highly versatile re-usable booster concept for which two US patents have been awarded. Each of these patents identifies one of the authors as sole inventor. It is particularly gratifying that two of the original engineering papers involved in this concept have been granted coveted awards in astronautics; namely the Society of Automotive Engineers' Colwell Merit Award and the British Interplanetary Society's Golovine Award.

Clearly, the development of a rocket-transportation system depends in large measure upon the potential market. Many billions of dollars will be required before this can acquire operational status; but three potential markets are possible, namely, supply missions into Earth-orbit, and military and commercial point-to-point transportation on Earth.

Any large rocket booster designed from its inception with sufficient inherent flexibility to capture a large portion of at least two of these markets could justify the enormous expenditures required for research and development. Therefore, although due emphasis is placed on using recoverable rocket boosters for transporting men and supplies into orbit, to the Moon, and to the planets, this book devotes much attention to the possibilities for rocket travel within the confines of our own world.

Man's commitment of his intellect, energies, and resources to space travel was natural once he had extensively exploited the three other media of transportation. This new frontier of space constitutes the only remaining means for satisfying man's insatiable compulsion to explore, discover the unknown, and conquer the unattained.

Man has travelled on Earth's oceans for the past 8,000 years, on wheeled land vehicles during the past 5,000 years, and in the Earth's atmosphere for the past 50 years. Each mode of transportation gave rise to mechanisms and devices or remarkable sophistication and complexity which burst the boundaries of human knowledge and experience. The rocket transport will be no exception.

The Color Pages

The 80 colour pages which follow illustrate some of the exciting new opportunities for space technology which may affect our lives over the next quarter of a century. They include a foretaste of observations that will be routinely made of our own planet helping to exploit natural resources such as minerals, oil, gas, water, agriculture and marine life as well as giving timely warning of natural disasters such as damaging storms, floods and forest fires.

New types of spacecraft are illustrated which allow men to conduct original research in the weightless environment of space, beginning with Russia's Soyuz spacecraft and America's Orbiting Workshop of the Apollo Applications Programme (AAP). Designs for manned space stations capable of extending many areas of science and technology – including the processing of materials under weightlessness – show the potential of routine space missions. Keeping such orbital platforms supplied demands a new breed of re-usable launch vehicles which operate on the principle of conventional aircraft using wings, lifting bodies or VTOL (vertical take-off and landing) technique. They will help to evolve revolutionary systems of rocket transportation on Earth.

All the future projects shown on these pages have been the subject of detailed study by major aerospace companies and therefore represent some of the most advanced thinking at the *Frontiers of Space*.

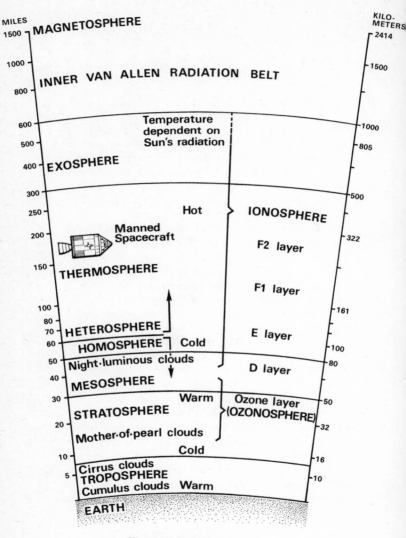

The Earth's Atmosphere

(*Above*) television picture of the Earth from 22,300 miles (35,880 km.) above the Amazon River, obtained by the third Applications Technology Satellite. South America is visible at the centre. Clockwise from upper left are North America, the Greenland ice cap, southern Spain, and the west coast of Africa. Clouds blanket Antarctica (see page 103). (*Below*) Indian sub-continent and Ceylon as photographed by Gemini 11 astronauts from an altitude of about 500 miles (805 km.) (see page 102).

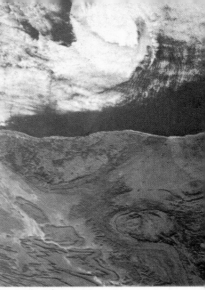

Our world from space. *(Above, left)* eastern tip of the Arabian Peninsula from Gemini 4. Airport (arrowed) is visible on the original photograph (see page 99). *(Right)* well-developed vortex (arrowed) caused by windshear at the coastal prominence of Ras Rhir, Morocco, from Gemini 5 (see page 102). *(Below, left)* Sudan, showing White Nile and Blue Nile Rivers below Khartoum; *(right)* east coast of the United States between Savannah and Brunswick, Georgia, from Apollo 6 at 115 miles (185 km.). Jet contrails can be seen over the Atlantic, arrowed (see page 103).

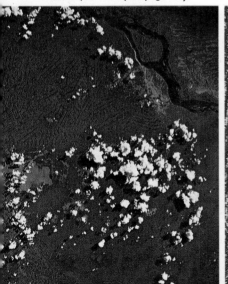

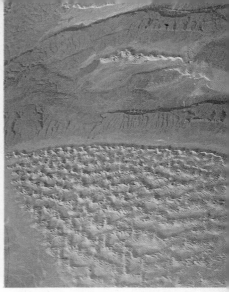

(*Above, left*) the greater New Orleans area, including parts of Louisiana and Mississippi, from Apollo 7 at 109 miles (175 km.). Note 25-mile (40 km.) causeway across Lake Pontchartrain. (*Right*) Tifernine Dunes in Algeria, south of Fort Flatters. (*Below, left*) Great Barrier Reef, Cape Melvile, Queensland, from Apollo 7 at 172 miles (277 km.). On the mainland forest fires are visible (see page 217). (*Right*) vegetation in Texas stimulated by rainfall the previous evening indicated by dark areas (see page 106).

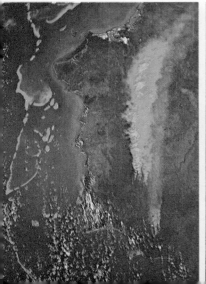

Orbiting laboratories can open up the world's natural resources to routine inspection, including agricultural crops. The potential is seen in this remarkable infra-red photograph from an aircraft of potato fields, indicating the presence of plant disease before it is detectable on the ground. Healthy potato plants, of high infra-red reflectance, show red; dark areas are potatoes with blight (see page 106).

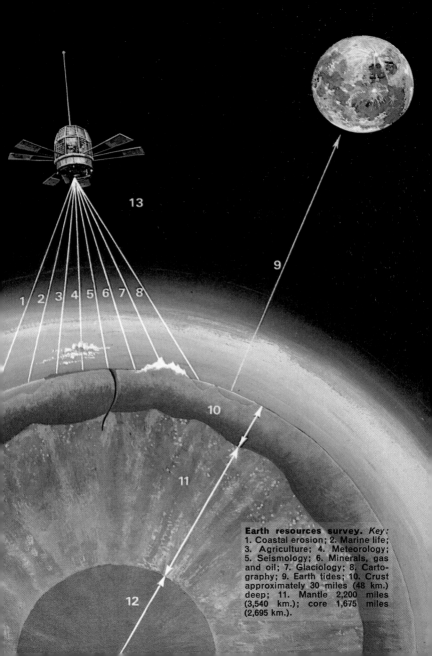

Earth resources survey. *Key:* 1. Coastal erosion; 2. Marine life; 3. Agriculture; 4. Meteorology; 5. Seismology; 6. Minerals, gas and oil; 7. Glaciology; 8. Cartography; 9. Earth tides; 10. Crust approximately 30 miles (48 km.) deep; 11. Mantle 2,200 miles (3,540 km.); core 1,675 miles (2,695 km.).

Kennedy Space
Center, Florida,
showing roads,
bridges and cause-
ways, from Gemini 7
(see page 101).
Conjunction of high-
ways leading to Fort
Worth *(left of centre)*
and Dallas *(right)* in
the State of Texas,
from Apollo 6 at 138
miles (222 km.) altitude
(see page 101).

Salton Sea area of California from Gemini 5 at 400 miles (644 km.).
Namib Desert along the Skeleton Coast of southwest Africa from a height of 200 miles (322 km.). Note sand-hooks caused by winds sweeping sand off the seif-type dunes into the Atlantic (see page 103).

(Above) **Great Bahama Banks** from Gemini 5 showing underwater features in the coral banks. Exuma Sound, near centre, drops abruptly to a depth of 8,000 ft (2,438 m.) (see page 108).

(Below) how snow cover in remote mountain areas can be assessed from space is shown in this Gemini 5 picture of the Himalayas which also sweeps across parts of China, India, Pakistan, Kashmir, and Afghanistan (see page 107).

(Above) Apollo 8 astronauts took this striking picture of Earth during their homeward journey from the Moon on 26 December 1968. North Pole is at about 11 o'clock. South America is at the centre and North America at upper left. A small portion of the bulge of West Africa can be seen near the sunset terminator. (Below) astronaut Frank Borman's famous picture of the rising Earth from Apollo 8 as the craft emerged from behind the Moon on its first orbit. The lunar horizon is about 485 miles (780 km.) from the spacecraft. On planet Earth the sunset terminator bisects Africa. Vertical Moon photos from Apollo 8 are on page 85.

Automatic docking of Cosmos 186 (*right*) **and Cosmos 188.** *Key:* 1. Docking units; 2. Scanning and homing antennae; 3. Extensible solar panels; 4. Radio antennae. Re-entry modules from both craft were recovered in the Soviet Union.

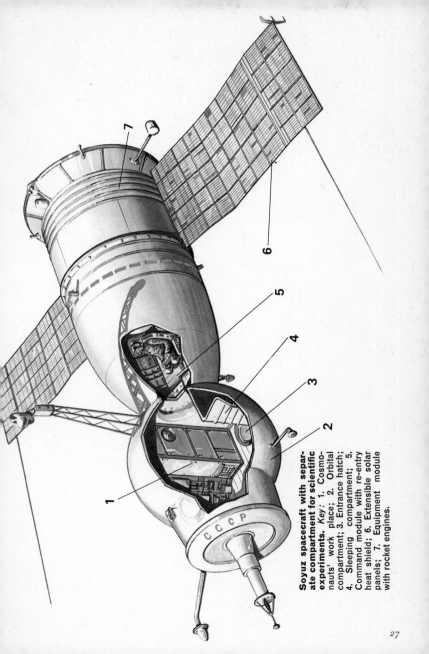

Soyuz spacecraft with separate compartment for scientific experiments. *Key*: 1. Cosmonauts' work place; 2. Orbital compartment; 3. Entrance hatch; 4. Sleeping compartment; 5. Command module with re-entry heat shield; 6. Extensible solar panels; 7. Equipment module with rocket engines.

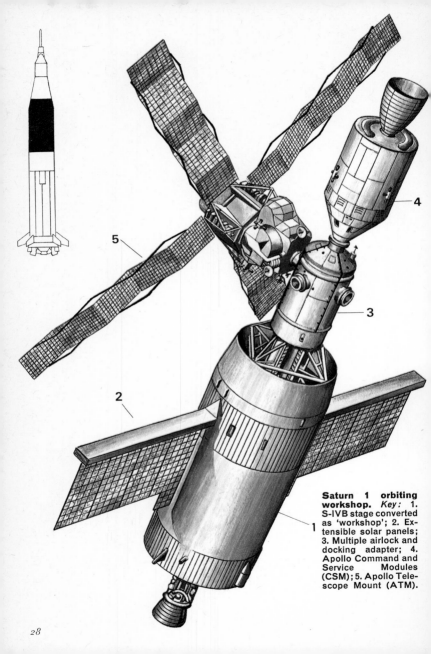

Saturn 1 orbiting workshop. *Key:* 1. S-IVB stage converted as 'workshop'; 2. Extensible solar panels; 3. Multiple airlock and docking adapter; 4. Apollo Command and Service Modules (CSM); 5. Apollo Telescope Mount (ATM).

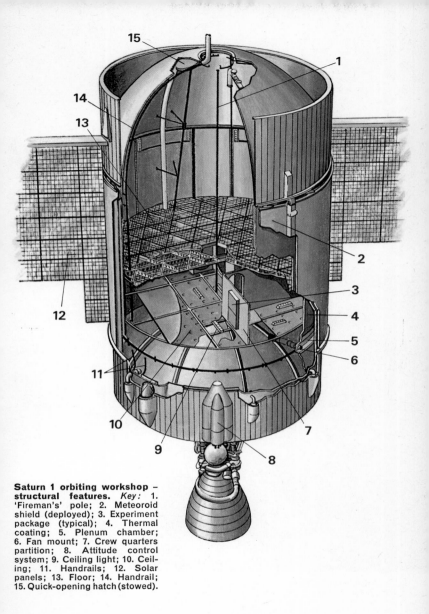

Saturn 1 orbiting workshop – structural features. *Key:* 1. 'Fireman's' pole; 2. Meteoroid shield (deployed); 3. Experiment package (typical); 4. Thermal coating; 5. Plenum chamber; 6. Fan mount; 7. Crew quarters partition; 8. Attitude control system; 9. Ceiling light; 10. Ceiling; 11. Handrails; 12. Solar panels; 13. Floor; 14. Handrail; 15. Quick-opening hatch (stowed).

Artist's impression of the complete Saturn 1 orbiting workshop in orbit.
(*Below*) the two-storey workshop made from the empty fuel tank of a Saturn
S-IVB rocket stage; (*above*) Apollo spacecraft docked for the transfer of
astronauts; (*top right*) Apollo Telescope Mount (ATM) with its cruciform of
solar cell panels for astronaut astronomy. The various components are
launched separately and docked together.

Engineering mockup of Saturn 1 orbiting workshop. *(Top left)* engineer-astronaut at control panel; *(right)* installing equipment. Floor of workshop is pre-installed metal grating and inside wall partitions are fabric. Astronauts connect the fabric compartment dividers to pre-fitted metal poles. *(Below, left)* demonstrating workshop equipment; *(right)* checking workshop-installed items.

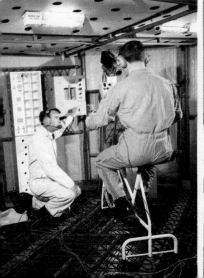

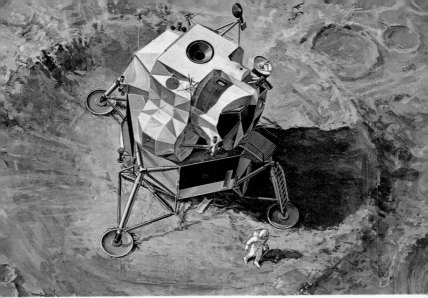

(*Above*) artist's impression of Apollo Lunar Module on the Moon. (*Below*) mockup of Apollo Telescope Mount (ATM) which employs basic structure of the Lunar Module ascent stage. Alongside is part of the S-IVB stage to which the ATM is docked in orbit.

(Above) discarded S-IVB stage as photographed off the coast of Florida by the Apollo 7 astronauts. A modification of this rocket forms the basis of the Saturn 1 orbiting workshop illustrated on pages 28–31. (Below) McDonnell-Douglas proposal for an advanced orbiting workshop in which six astronauts could remain for one year.

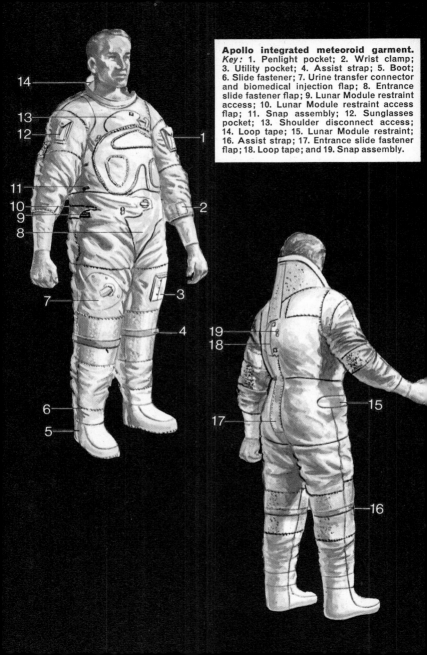

Apollo integrated meteoroid garment.
Key: 1. Penlight pocket; 2. Wrist clamp;
3. Utility pocket; 4. Assist strap; 5. Boot.
6. Slide fastener; 7. Urine transfer connector
and biomedical injection flap; 8. Entrance
slide fastener flap; 9. Lunar Module restraint
access; 10. Lunar Module restraint access
flap; 11. Snap assembly; 12. Sunglasses
pocket; 13. Shoulder disconnect access;
14. Loop tape; 15. Lunar Module restraint;
16. Assist strap; 17. Entrance slide fastener
flap; 18. Loop tape; and 19. Snap assembly.

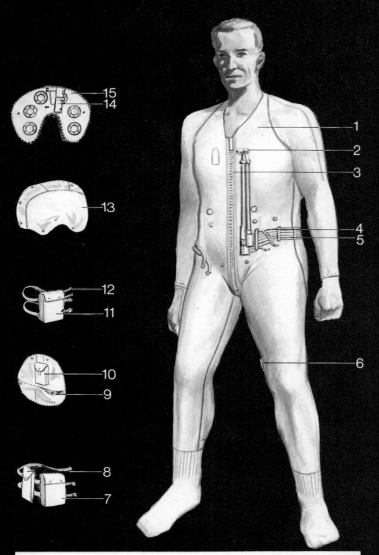

(Right) **Liquid-cooling garment worn beneath EVA spacesuit.** *Key:* 1. Liquid-cooling garment; 2. Connector; 3. Zipper; 4. Manifold; 5. Tygon tubing; 6. Dosimeter. *(Left,* see also page 36 for assembly*)*; 7. Checklist; 8. Scissors pocket; 9. Lanyard pocket; 10. Active dosimeter pocket; 11. Data list pocket; 12. Belt assembly; 13. Connector cover; 14. Hold down strap access panel, and 15. Chest cover.

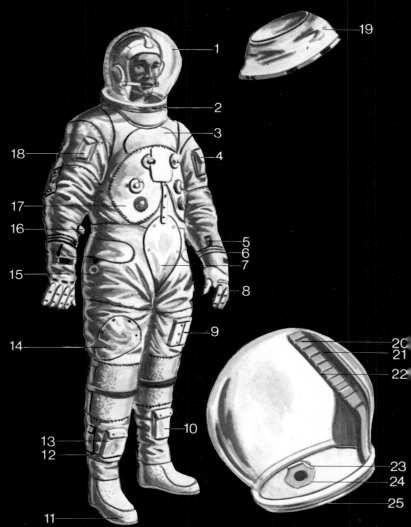

Apollo spacesuit assembly. *Key:* 1. Pressure helmet assembly; 2. Helmet attachment ring; 3. Shoulder disconnect access; 4. Penlight pocket; 5. Pressure relief valve; 6. Wrist disconnect; 7. Entrance slide fastener flap; 8. Pressure glove; 9. Utility pocket; 10. Data list pocket; 11. Integrated thermal meteoroid garment boot; 12. Checklist pocket; 13. Scissors pocket; 14. Urine transfer connector, biomedical injection flap, and donning lanyard pocket; 15. Lunar Module restraint ring; 16. Pressure gauge; 17. Chest cover; 18. Sunglasses pocket; 19. Neck dam. 20. Spacer; 21. Recess; 22. Vent pad; 23. Feed port; 24. Feed port cover; and 25. Neck ring (extravehicular gloves and lunar overshoes shown opposite.)

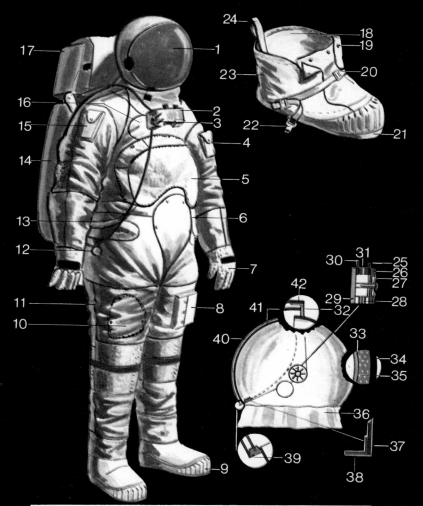

Apollo extravehicular suit. *Key:* 1. Extravehicular visor; 2. Backpack control box; 3. Oxygen purge system actuator; 4. Penlight pocket; 5. Connector cover; 6. Communication, ventilation, and liquid cooling umbilicals; 7. Extravehicular glove; 8. Utility pocket; 9. Lunar overshoe; 10. Urine transfer connector, biomedical injection, dosimeter access flap and donning lanyard pocket; 11. Integrated thermal meteoroid garment; 12. Lunar Module restraint ring; 13. Oxygen purge system umbilical; 14. Backpack; 15. Sunglasses pocket; 16. Backpack support straps; 17. Oxygen purge system; 18. Liner and insulation assembly; 19. Snap fastener; 20. Strap assembly; 21. Sole assembly; 22. Latch; 23. Shell assembly; 24. Donning strap; 25. Sun visor; 26. Friction plate; 27. Hinge adjustment spring; 28. Washer; 29. Base; 30. Protective visor; 31. Spacer; 32. Light seal; 33. Membrane; 34. Shell; 35. Insulation cross-section; 36. Visor-suit interface collar; 37. Sun visor; 38. Tab; 39. Light seal; 40. Sun visor; 41. Protective visor; and 42. Sun visor.

(Above) Vostok launch vehicle displayed on the transporter-erector at Le Bourget in 1967. A total of 20 main thrust chambers and 12 swivel-mounted vernier chambers operated at lift-off, burning liquid oxygen and kerosene propellants. The four strap-on boosters were jettisoned during the thrust programme. (Below) close-up of thrust chambers.

First Soviet- and US-manned launch vehicles compared to scale. *(Left)* Vostok launcher. Length 124·7 ft (38 m.); base width over stabilizers 33·8 ft (10·3 m.); length sustainer core 91·8 ft (28 m.); maximum diameter sustainer core 9·7 ft (2·95 m.); length booster (4) 2·3 ft (19 m.); maximum diameter boosters 9·8 ft (3 m.); length final stage with nose shroud 32·8 ft (10 m.); weight Vostok spacecraft 10,418 lb (4,725 kg.) total thrust all stages 1,322,770 lb (600,000 kg.). *(Right)* Mercury-Atlas. Developed from 'first-generation' ICBM. Employed two booster engines in jettisonable fairing, one central sustainer, and two swivelling verniers; propellant liquid oxygen and RP-1 (kerosene). Length including escape tower 94·3 ft; tank diameter 10 ft (3·05 m.); width over boost fairing 16 ft (4·9 m.). Weight Mercury (MA-6) capsule 4,265 lb (1,937 kg.) at lift-off, 2,987 lb (1,355 kg.) in orbit. Total launch weight 260,000 lb (117,930 kg.); launch thrust 367,000 lb (166,470 kg.).

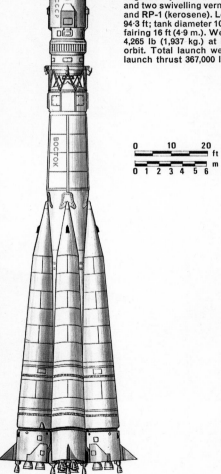

```
0        10        20
|‾‾|‾‾|‾‾|‾‾|‾‾|‾‾|      ft
|‾|‾|‾|‾|‾|‾|‾|         m
0  1  2  3  4  5  6
```

At the Kennedy Space Center, Florida, Saturn 5 with Apollo spacecraft attached emerges from the Vertical Assembly Building *en route* for the launch pad some 3 miles (4·8 km.) distant.

Saturn 5 blasts off from the Kennedy Space Center to send the manned Apollo 7 spacecraft into Earth-orbit. In this vehicle astronauts Walter Schirra, Donn Eisele, and Walter Cunningham, qualified basic equipment for subsequent manned missions to the Moon.

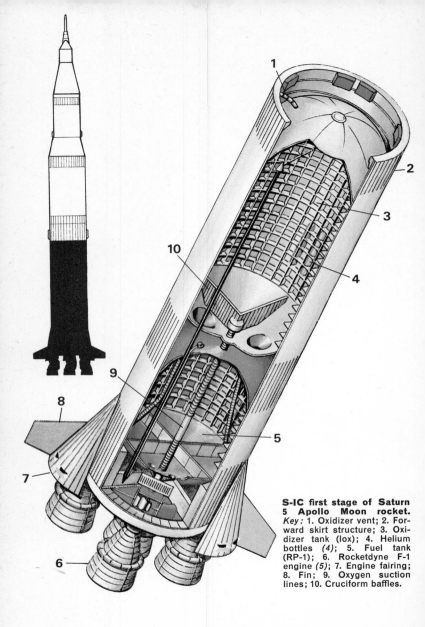

S-IC first stage of Saturn 5 Apollo Moon rocket.
Key: 1. Oxidizer vent; 2. Forward skirt structure; 3. Oxidizer tank (lox); 4. Helium bottles *(4)*; 5. Fuel tank (RP-1); 6. Rocketdyne F-1 engine *(5)*; 7. Engine fairing; 8. Fin; 9. Oxygen suction lines; 10. Cruciform baffles.

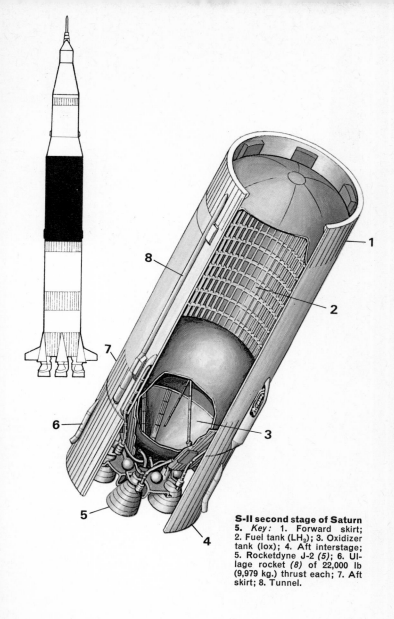

S-II second stage of Saturn 5. *Key:* 1. Forward skirt; 2. Fuel tank (LH₂); 3. Oxidizer tank (lox); 4. Aft interstage; 5. Rocketdyne J-2 *(5)*; 6. Ullage rocket *(8)* of 22,000 lb (9,979 kg.) thrust each; 7. Aft skirt; 8. Tunnel.

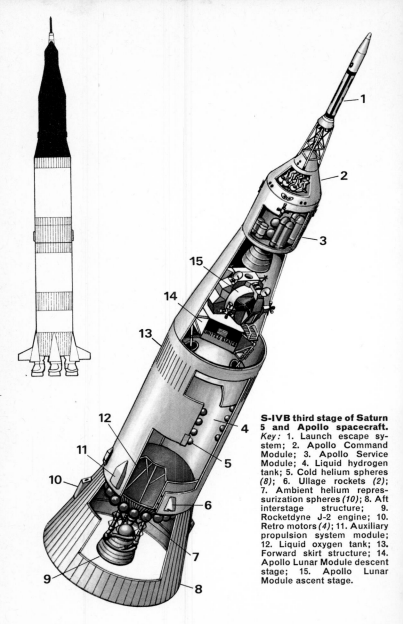

S-IVB third stage of Saturn 5 and Apollo spacecraft. *Key:* 1. Launch escape system; 2. Apollo Command Module; 3. Apollo Service Module; 4. Liquid hydrogen tank; 5. Cold helium spheres *(8)*; 6. Ullage rockets *(2)*; 7. Ambient helium repressurization spheres *(10)*; 8. Aft interstage structure; 9. Rocketdyne J-2 engine; 10. Retro motors *(4)*; 11. Auxiliary propulsion system module; 12. Liquid oxygen tank; 13. Forward skirt structure; 14. Apollo Lunar Module descent stage; 15. Apollo Lunar Module ascent stage.

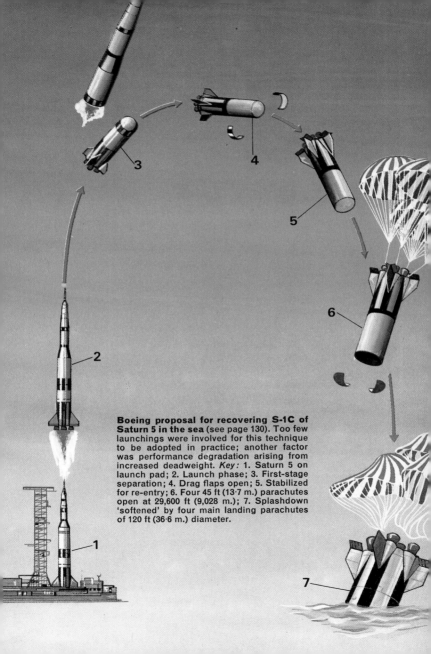

Boeing proposal for recovering S-1C of Saturn 5 in the sea (see page 130). Too few launchings were involved for this technique to be adopted in practice; another factor was performance degradation arising from increased deadweight. *Key:* 1. Saturn 5 on launch pad; 2. Launch phase; 3. First-stage separation; 4. Drag flaps open; 5. Stabilized for re-entry; 6. Four 45 ft (13·7 m.) parachutes open at 29,600 ft (9,028 m.); 7. Splashdown 'softened' by four main landing parachutes of 120 ft (36·6 m.) diameter.

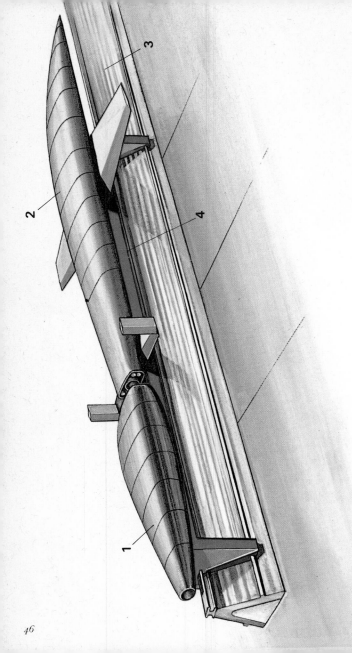

Sänger-Bredt antipodal bomber and captive booster on horizontal launch rail (1938–42 concept). *Key:* 1. Captive rocket booster of 600 tonnes thrust; 2. Rocket aircraft of 100 tonnes thrust; 3. Monorail track 1·8 miles (3·0 km.) long; and 4. Sled carriage.

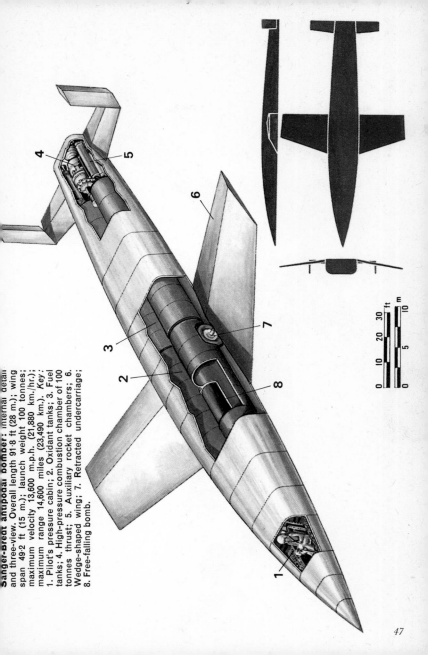

Sänger-Bredt antipodal bomber: internal detail and three-view. Overall length 91·8 ft (28 m.); wing span 49·2 ft (15 m.); launch weight 100 tonnes; maximum velocity 13,600 m.p.h. (21,880 km./hr.); maximum range 14,600 miles (23,490 km.). *Key:* 1. Pilot's pressure cabin; 2. Oxidant tanks; 3. Fuel tanks; 4. High-pressure combustion chamber of 100 tonnes thrust; 5. Auxiliary rocket chambers; 6. Wedge-shaped wing; 7. Retracted undercarriage; 8. Free-falling bomb.

47

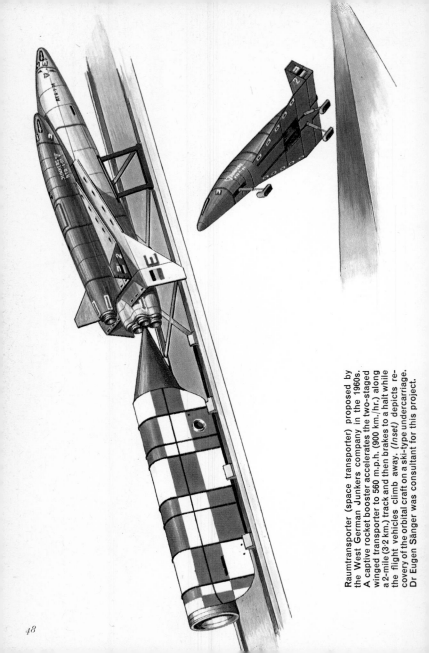

Raumtransporter (space transporter) proposed by the West German Junkers company in the 1960s. A captive rocket booster accelerates the two-staged winged transporter to 560 m.p.h. (900 km./hr.) along a 2-mile (3·2 km.) track and then brakes to a halt while the flight vehicles climb away. (*Inset*) depicts recovery of the orbital craft on a ski-type undercarriage. Dr Eugen Sänger was consultant for this project.

48

The two flight stages separate high in the atmosphere. While the larger vehicle returns immediately to land on a runway, the smaller craft proceeds into orbit. After the mission the orbital craft – made largely of nickel steel with ablative coatings – makes a glide re-entry into Earth's atmosphere. Its landing is depicted on the opposite page. Launch weight would be 150–250 tonnes and payload to low orbit 2–3 tonnes.

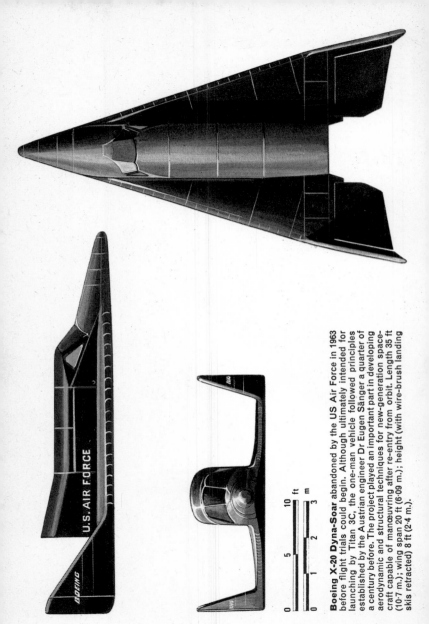

Boeing X-20 Dyna-Soar abandoned by the US Air Force in 1963 before flight trials could begin. Although ultimately intended for launching by Titan 3C, the one-man vehicle followed principles established by the Austrian engineer Dr Eugen Sänger a quarter of a century before. The project played an important part in developing aerodynamic and structural techniques for new-generation space-craft capable of manoeuvring after re-entry from orbit. Length 35 ft (10·7 m.); wing span 20 ft (6·09 m.); height (with wire-brush landing skis retracted) 8 ft (2·4 m.).

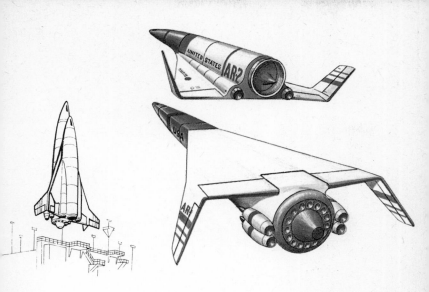

(Above) **Vertical take-off of 'Astrorocket'** studied by the Martin Company in the early 1960s in which turbojets under wings of first stage assist manœuvre and landing after depletion of rocket propellants. Top stage makes glide return and landing from orbit. *(Below)* Franco-German space transporter concept by Entwicklungsring Nord (ERNO), Nord-Aviation and SNECMA, in which a winged orbital craft is carried beneath a large air-breathing booster which takes off and lands conventionally on a runway.

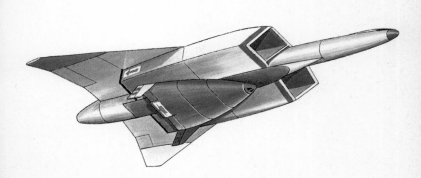

MUSTARD, by British Aircraft Corporation, envisaged three winged and piloted vehicles launched together as a unit with all engines firing. The outer pair of vehicles serve as boosters and transfer fuel to the third which continues into orbit.

When fuel transfer is completed the **MUSTARD** boost units break away and return to base under turbojet propulsion. After the centre vehicle has delivered its payload into a low orbit, it begins re-entry about 11,000 miles (17,700 km.) from base where it lands like a conventional aircraft.

Lifting-body technology evolves. *(Above)* the NASA/Northrop M2-F2 installed on the wing pylon of the B-52 parent. Test flights begin at 45,000 ft (13,700 m.) above the Mojave Desert. *(Below)* the NASA/Northrop HL-10 makes a perfect touchdown on Rogers Dry Lake.

(*Above*) the USAF/Martin X-24A lifting body also test-flown from a B-52 parent.
(*Below*) Lockheed two-man lifting-body concept with variable-geometry 'swing wings' to assist landing.

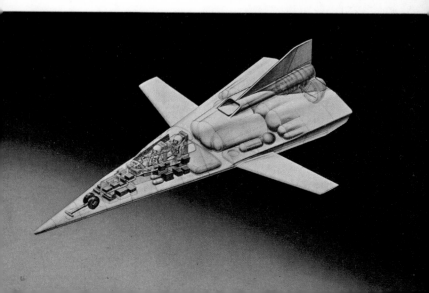

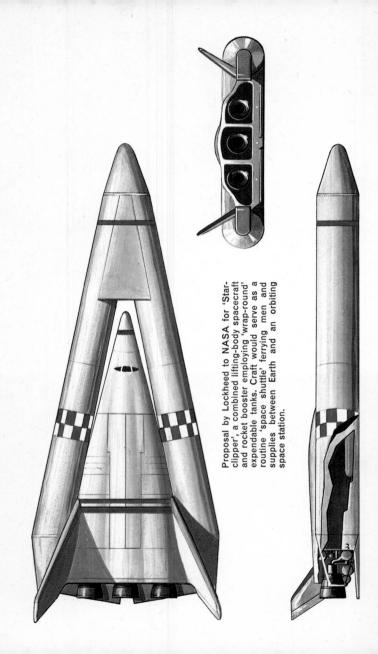

Proposal by Lockheed to NASA for 'Star-clipper', a combined lifting-body spacecraft and rocket booster employing 'wrap-round' expendable tanks. Craft would serve as a routine 'space shuttle' ferrying men and supplies between Earth and an orbiting space station.

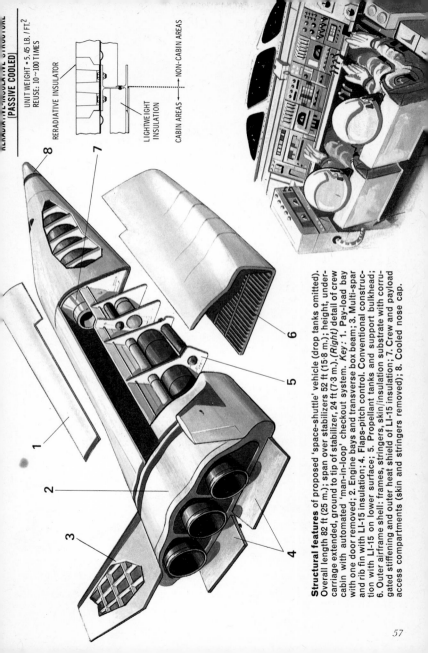

ABLATIVE-INSULATIVE STRUCTURE **(PASSIVE COOLED)**

UNIT WEIGHT = 5·45 LB. / FT.^{2}
REUSE: 10~100 TIMES

RERADIATIVE INSULATOR

LIGHTWEIGHT INSULATION

CABIN AREAS → NON-CABIN AREAS

Structural features of proposed 'space-shuttle' vehicle (drop tanks omitted). Overall length 82 ft (25 m.); span over stabilizers 52 ft (15·8 m.); height, undercarriage extended, ground to tip of stabilizer, 24 ft (7·3 m.). *(Right)* detail of crew cabin with automated 'man-in-loop' checkout system. *Key:* 1. Pay-load bay with one door removed; 2. Engine bays and transverse box beam; 3. Multi-spar and rib fin with LI-15 insulation; 4. Flaps-pitch control. Conventional construction with LI-15 on lower surface; 5. Propellant tanks and support bulkhead; 6. Outer airframe shell: frames, stringers, skin/insulation substrate with corrugated stiffening and outer heat shield of LI-15 insulation; 7. Crew and payload access compartments (skin and stringers removed); 8. Cooled nose cap.

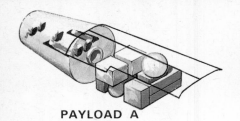

PAYLOAD A

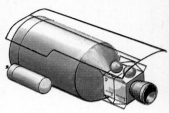

PAYLOAD B

PAYLOAD MODULE

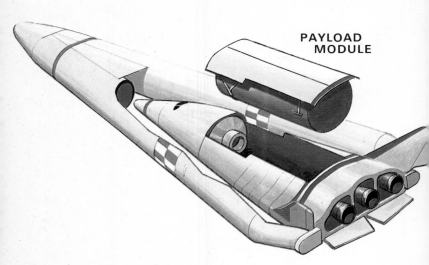

PAYLOAD C

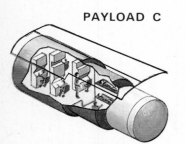

PAYLOAD D

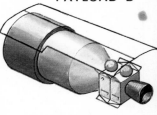

'Space-shuttle' alternative payloads. *Payload A* cargo 7,260 lb (3,293 kg.), personnel *(7)* 1,260 lb (571 kg.); *Payload B* cargo 19,900 lb (9,026 kg.); *Payload C* equipment 11,760 lb (5,334 kg.), personnel *(7)* 1,260 lb (571 kg.); *Payload D* cargo 22,000 lb (9,979 kg.). Total launch weight: 719,400 lb (326,320 kg.); propellant weight 589,800 lb (267,533 kg.); drop tank weight 28,600 lb (12,973 kg.). Lifting-body inert weight 40,000–44,000 lb (18,144–19,958 kg.); propellant weight 50,000 lb (2,268 kg.).

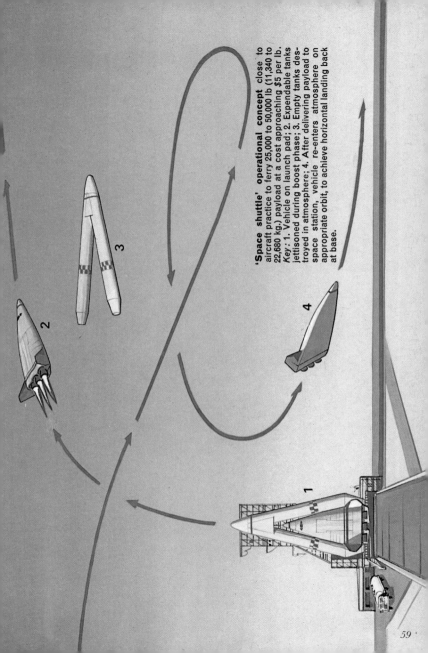

'Space shuttle' operational concept close to aircraft practice to ferry 25,000 to 50,000 lb (11,340 to 22,680 kg.) payload at a cost approaching $5 per lb. *Key*: 1. Vehicle on launch pad; 2. Expendable tanks jettisoned during boost phase; 3. Empty tanks destroyed in atmosphere; 4. After delivering payload to space station, vehicle re-enters atmosphere on appropriate orbit, to achieve horizontal landing back at base.

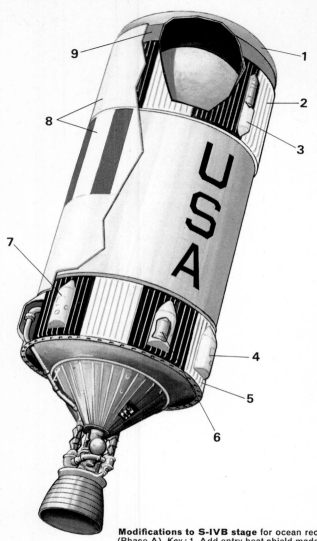

Modifications to S-IVB stage for ocean recovery (Phase A). *Key:* 1. Add entry heat shield made from honeycomb sandwich with DC 325 thermal protection; 2. Forward skirt; 3. Add *(4)* orbital retro-rockets, support structure and fairings; 4. APS module (existing); 5. Aft skirt; 6. Add *(4)* landing retro-rockets support structure and fairings; 7. Add *(3)* ballutes and *(3)* main parachutes and stowage fairings.

Artist's impression of S-IVB stage during terminal phase of recovery. Slowed by retro-rockets and protected by a heat shield during re-entry, the 58 ft (17·7 m.) long S-IVB would be lowered into the sea beneath three 80 ft (24·4 m.) diameter parachutes. Proposal was made to evaluate feasibility of recovering ballistic rocket stages from orbit.

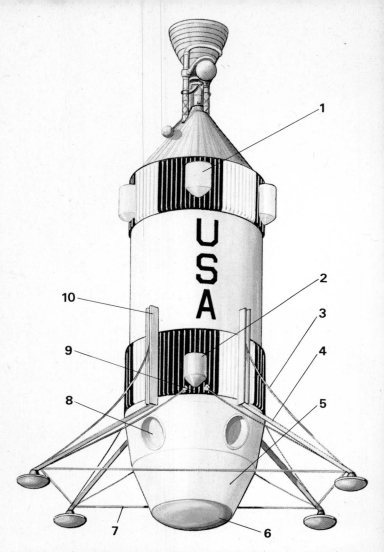

Land recovery of modified S-IVB stage (Phase B). *Key:* 1. 'Ballute' and parachute stowage canisters *(3)*; canister weight 300 lb (136 kg.) total, 28 ft (8·5 m.) diameter 'ballute,' weight 1,800 (816 kg.) total, 124 ft (37·8 m.) diameter parachute weight 750 lb (340 kg.) total; 2. Orbital retro-motors *(4)* weight 920 lb (417 kg.) including 650 lb (295 kg.) propellants; 3. Deploy cable; 4. Stabilizing arms *(4)*; 5. Crushable honeycomb; 6. Heat shield; 7. Load-distributing cable; 8. Landing pad stowage (on adapter); 9. IU (existing); 10. Guide rails (attached to forward skirt).

S-IVB recovery sequence. Operations: 1. Standard attitude maintained in orbit (vehicle parallel to local horizon), nose fairings jettison; 2. Ground-commanded retroignition; 3. Stabilize with APS during descent; 4. Deploy three 28 ft (8·5 m.) ballutes at 350,000 ft (106,680 m.) altitude; 5. Three 124 ft (37·8 m.) main parachutes extracted by ballutes at 30,000 ft (9,144 m.) altitude and 210 ft/sec. (64 m./sec.) velocity approximately; 6. Separate ballutes; 7. Deploy stabilizing legs; 8. Landing at 40 ft/sec. (12·2 m./sec.) and release of parachutes.

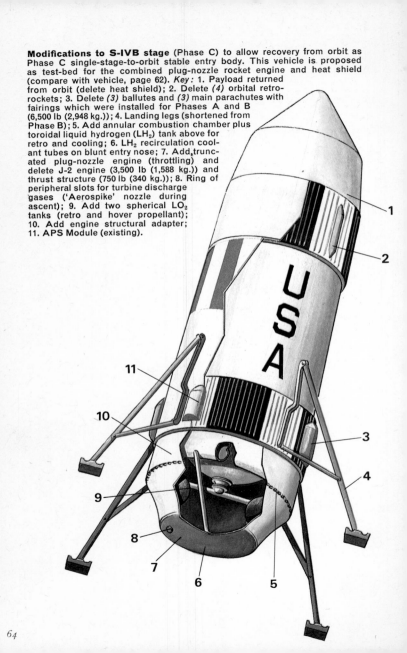

Modifications to S-IVB stage (Phase C) to allow recovery from orbit as Phase C single-stage-to-orbit stable entry body. This vehicle is proposed as test-bed for the combined plug-nozzle rocket engine and heat shield (compare with vehicle, page 62). *Key:* 1. Payload returned from orbit (delete heat shield); 2. Delete *(4)* orbital retro-rockets; 3. Delete *(3)* ballutes and *(3)* main parachutes with fairings which were installed for Phases A and B (6,500 lb (2,948 kg.)); 4. Landing legs (shortened from Phase B); 5. Add annular combustion chamber plus toroidal liquid hydrogen (LH_2) tank above for retro and cooling; 6. LH_2 recirculation coolant tubes on blunt entry nose; 7. Add truncated plug-nozzle engine (throttling) and delete J-2 engine (3,500 lb (1,588 kg.)) and thrust structure (750 lb (340 kg.)); 8. Ring of peripheral slots for turbine discharge gases ('Aerospike' nozzle during ascent); 9. Add two spherical LO_2 tanks (retro and hover propellant); 10. Add engine structural adapter; 11. APS Module (existing).

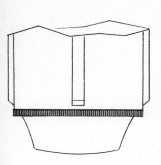
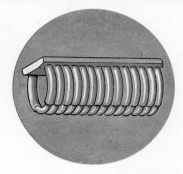

SEGMENTED TOROIDAL COMBUSTION CHAMBER

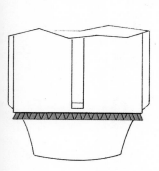

CIRCULAR MODULE CLUSTER

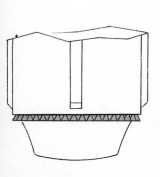

ELLIPTICAL MODULE CLUSTER

Alternative designs of combustion chambers for re-usable launch vehicles employing regeneratively cooled, truncated plug nozzles, both for ascent propulsion and as a heat shield, during re-entry from orbit. For typical vehicle applications see pages 64 and 66–68, 70–76, 78–82, 86–88, 90; for working principle of plug nozzle see page 69.

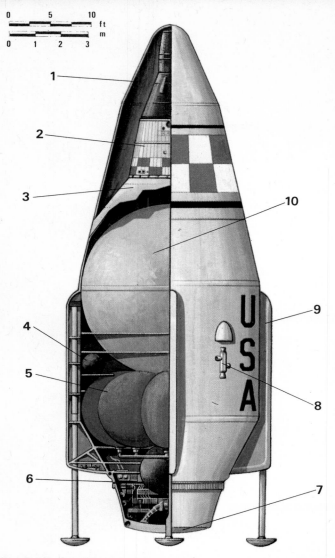

Saturn Application Single-Stage-To-Orbit (SASSTO). *Key:* 1. Optional fairing around two-man Gemini capsule; 2. Gemini adapter section; 3. Transition support structure; 4. Orbit injection/retro- and attitude-control propellant tanks *(6)*; 5. Toroidal liquid-oxygen tank; 6. Annular combustion chamber; 7. Truncated plug nozzle and re-entry heat shield; 8. Attitude-control system *(4)*; 9. Retractable landing legs *(4)*; 10. Spherical liquid-hydrogen propellant tank.

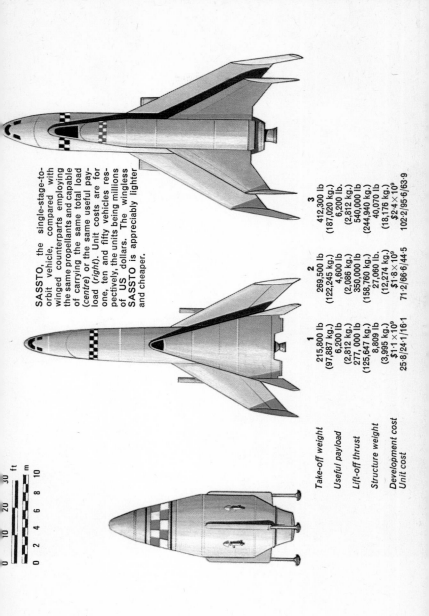

SASSTO, the single-stage-to-orbit vehicle, compared with winged counterparts employing the same propellants and capable of carrying the same total load (*centre*) or the same useful payload (*right*). Unit costs are for one, ten and fifty vehicles respectively, the units being millions of US dollars. The wingless SASSTO is appreciably lighter and cheaper.

	1	**2**	**3**
Take-off weight	215,800 lb (97,887 kg.)	269,500 lb (122,245 kg.)	412,300 lb (187,020 kg.)
Useful payload	6,200 lb (2,812 kg.)	4,600 lb (2,086 kg.)	6,200 lb. (2,812 kg.)
Lift-off thrust	277,000 lb (125,647 kg.)	350,000 lb (158,760 kg.)	540,000 lb (244,940 kg.)
Structure weight	8,809 lb (3,995 kg.)	27,060 lb. (12,274 kg.)	40,070 lb (18,176 kg.)
Development cost	$1·1×10⁹	$1·8×10⁹	$2·4×10⁹
Unit cost	25·8/24·1/16·1	71·2/66·6/44·5	102·2/95·6/63·9

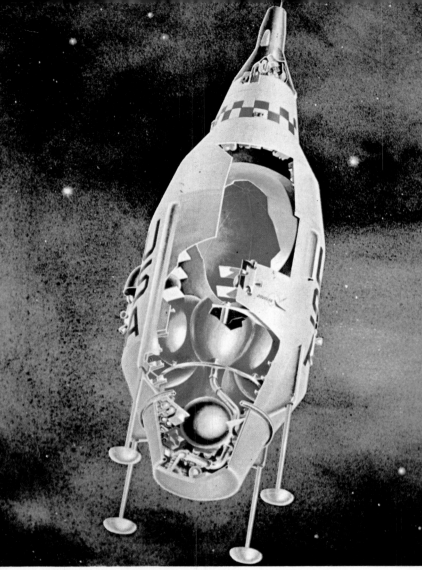

SASSTO (Saturn Application Single-Stage-to-Orbit) combined launch
vehicle and spacecraft. Only 62·3 ft (19 m.) tall, a single plug-nozzle engine
would serve both at launch and for soft-landing back on Earth after an orbital
mission. The craft – seen here with a Gemini two-man capsule – would be
recovered intact and could be used repeatedly. It would be particularly appropriate for ferry missions into Earth-orbit including the emergency rescue of
astronauts.

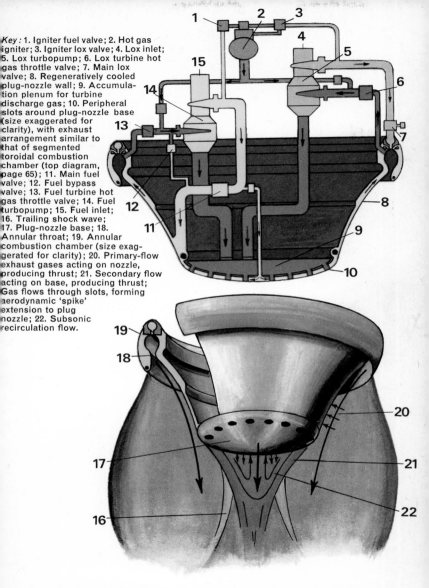

Key : 1. Igniter fuel valve; 2. Hot gas igniter; 3. Igniter lox valve; 4. Lox inlet; 5. Lox turbopump; 6. Lox turbine hot gas throttle valve; 7. Main lox valve; 8. Regeneratively cooled plug-nozzle wall; 9. Accumulation plenum for turbine discharge gas; 10. Peripheral slots around plug-nozzle base (size exaggerated for clarity), with exhaust arrangement similar to that of segmented toroidal combustion chamber (top diagram, page 65); 11. Main fuel valve; 12. Fuel bypass valve; 13. Fuel turbine hot gas throttle valve; 14. Fuel turbopump; 15. Fuel inlet; 16. Trailing shock wave; 17. Plug-nozzle base; 18. Annular throat; 19. Annular combustion chamber (size exaggerated for clarity); 20. Primary-flow exhaust gases acting on nozzle, producing thrust; 21. Secondary flow acting on base, producing thrust; Gas flows through slots, forming aerodynamic 'spike' extension to plug nozzle; 22. Subsonic recirculation flow.

Plug-nozzle 'Aerospike, engine (after Rocketdyne) adapted as re-entry heat shield: not to scale. Combustion chamber arrangement can be annular, as shown here, or segmented or clustered, as illustrated on page 65. The latter systems allow individual chamber groups to be switched on or off according to changing thrust requirements during flight.

69

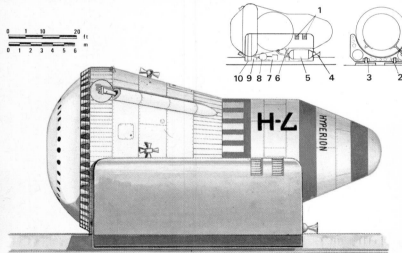

(Above) artist's impression of Hyperion sled launch. *(Below)* **Hyperion Rocket Sled.** *Key:* 1. Passenger-loading stairways *(4)*; 2. Sled 'tee' guide rails *(2)*; 3. Sled mechanical brake pads *(4)*; 4. Sled-braking retro-rockets *(2)*; 5. Retro-rocket propellant tanks *(2)*; 6. Retractable forward cradle support; 7. Ground-effect air compressor and blower; 8. Spherical retro-rocket propellant tanks *(4)*; 9. Quick-disconnect fittings *(6)*; 10. Fixed aft cradle support.

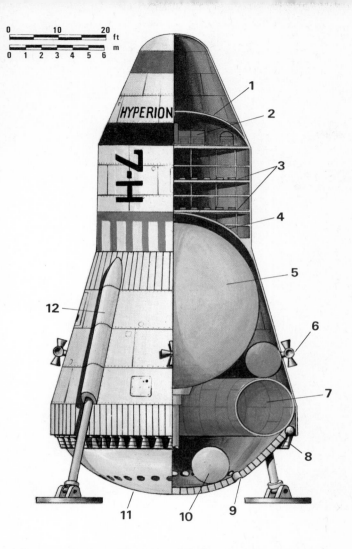

Hyperion passenger transport. *Key:* 1. Forward pressure bulkhead; 2. Cargo compartment; 3. Passenger compartment with 55 couches on each deck *(2)*; 4. Aft pressure bulkhead; 5. Spherical liquid-hydrogen propellant tank; 6. Auxiliary propulsion quad nozzles and tank *(4)*; 7. Toroidal liquid-oxygen tank; 8. Peripherally arranged main combustion chambers *(48)*; 9. Slots for 'Aerospike' nozzle-extension *(48)*; 10. Propellant tanks for orbital injection/retro and descent cooling *(4)*; 11. Re-entry heat shield cooled by liquid hydrogen; 12. Retractable landing legs *(4)*.

Re-usable Orbital Module - Booster and Utility Shuttle (ROMBUS). *Key :* 1. Payload 0·8 to 1·0 million lb to orbit; 2. Roll-control nozzle pairs *(4)*; 3. Vent lines for liquid hydrogen tanks *(8)*; 4. Propellant utilization probes *(8)*; 5. Booster centre body; 6. Fuel tank support fittings *(16)*; 7. Guidance and electronic package; 8. Attitude-control propellant tanks *(4)*; 9. Spherical oxidizer tank; 10. Anti-slosh baffles; 11. Fuel feed lines *(18)*; 12. Quick-disconnect fittings *(8)*; 13. Propellant turbopumps *(18)*; 14. Peripherally arranged combustion chambers *(36)*; 15. Oxidizer feed lines *(18)*; 16. Liquid hydrogen tank for entry cooling; 17. Turbine discharge lines *(18)*; 18. Turbine discharge port; 19. Oxidizer-tank-pressurization helium bottles *(4)*; 20. Propellant tank for landing retro-thrust; 21. Isentropic-expansion plug nozzle; 22. Retractable landing legs *(4)*; 23. Regeneration-cooling tubes; 24. Liquid oxygen tank sump; 25. Solid motors for thrust augmentation *(4)*; 26. Liquid hydrogen manifold; 27. Fuel manifold valve for liquid hydrogen tanks *(8)*; 28. Attitude-control propellant tanks *(4)*; 29. Centrebody recovery components; 30. Cylindrical liquid hydrogen fuel tanks *(8)*; 31. Tank-recovery thermal protection *(4)*.

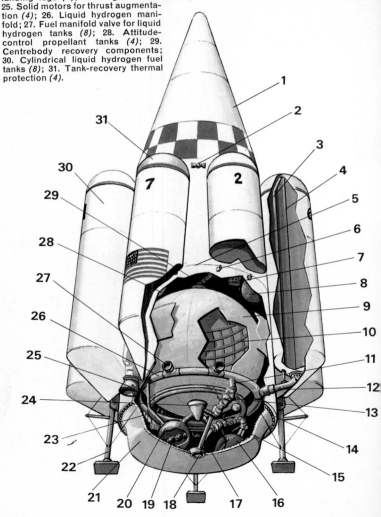

(Above) Rombus launch pad with water-filled acoustic limiter. After engine ignition water surface assumes parabolic contour. *(Below)* LH$_2$ tanks jettison, four at 130 sec. from launch, two more at 196 sec., and two at 300 sec. After leaving a massive payload in Earth-orbit, vehicle centrebody is recovered by combined use of parachutes and plug-nozzle retro-thrust.

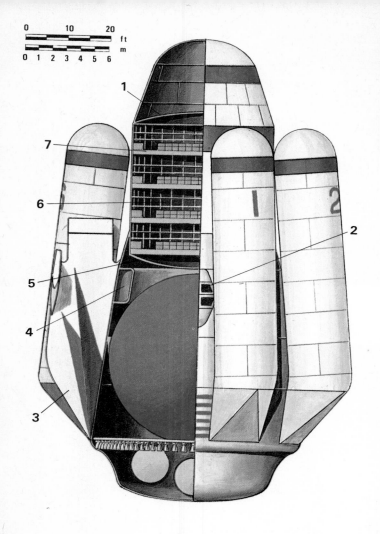

Pegasus Intercontinental Passenger Rocket. *Key:* 1. Forward pressure dome; 2. Two-man crew compartment; 3. Re-entry stabilization fins *(2)*; 4. Cargo compartment; 5. Aft pressure dome; 6. Pressurized cabin for passengers *(170)*; 7. Deck structure *(4)* with passenger couches *(43* each).

(Above) Pegasus during atmospheric re-entry uses the LH$_2$-cooled plug nozzle as a heat shield. The ballistic transport would convey 172 passengers and freight 7,456 miles (12,000 km.) in 39 min. without exceeding an acceleration of 3 g during either ascent or re-entry. At the arrival spaceport it would hover on rocket thrust during a soft landing in the vertical attitude. (Below) **Pegasus Passenger Compartment** Key : 1. Four-level passenger access doors (3); 2. Stairways (2) connecting four passenger decks; 3. Double-wall acoustic damping structure; 4. Luggage racks (9); 5. Re-entry stabilization fins (2).

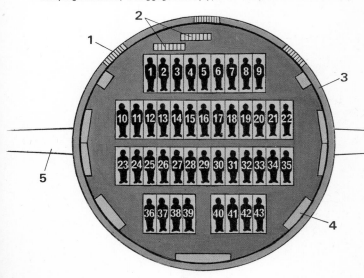

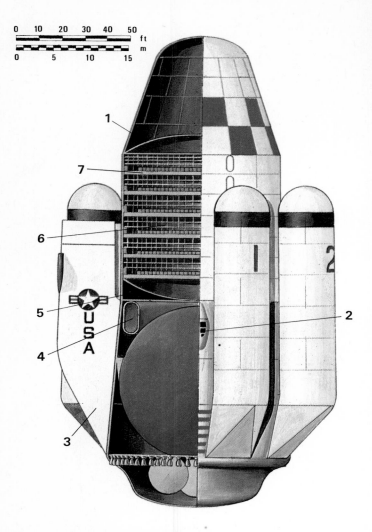

Ithacus Intercontinental Troop Transport. *Key:* 1. Forward pressure bulkhead; 2. Four-man crew compartment; 3. Re-entry stabilization fins *(2)*; 4. Cargo container; 5. Aft pressure bulkhead; 6. Pressurized cabin for troops *(1200)*; 7. Deck structure *(6)* with troop couches *(200 each)*.

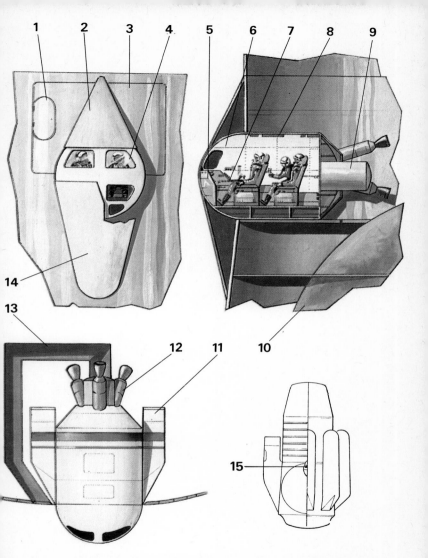

Ithacus four-man crew compartment. *Key:* 1. External door; 2. Ascent heat shield; 3. Jettisonable panel; 4. Windows *(6)*; 5. Control console; 6. Control panel; 7. Instrument panel; 8. Pressurized capsule with external compartment for parachute; 9. Air lock; 10. Spherical liquid oxygen tank of centrebody; 11. Stabilizing fins *(2)*; 12. Flight test emergency escape rockets *(3)*; 13. Access way to crew compartment; 14. Jettisonable re-entry heat shield; 15. Crew compartment location.

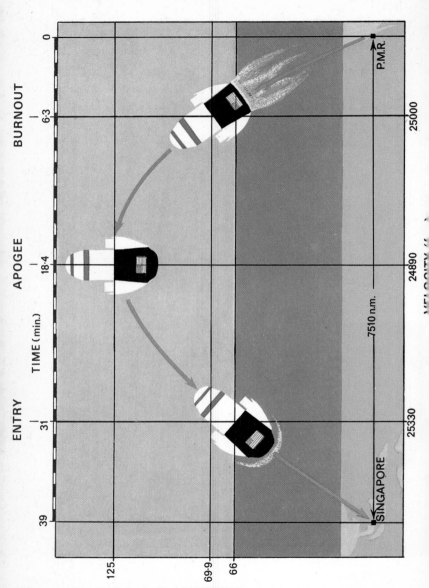

BURNOUT APOGEE ENTRY

0 6·3 18·4 31 39

TIME (min.)

P.M.R.

25000 24890 25330

7510 n.m.

SINGAPORE

VELOCITY (

125 69·9 66

ALTITUDE (n.m.)

Pegasus. Typical mission profile with launch and re-entry accelerations held to 3 *g* maxima.

78

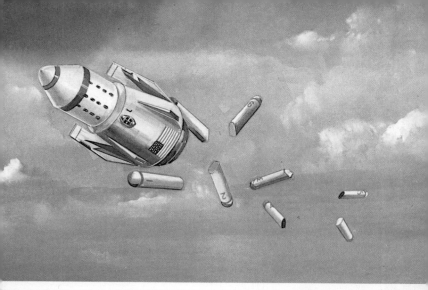

Normally Pegasus/Ithacus-type vehicles would ascend almost vertically during the first 70 sec. of flight. These pictures illustrate an emergency 'abort'. *(Above)* hydrogen fuel tanks jettison and liquid oxygen is pumped overboard from internal tank. *(Below)* turbopumps run by emergency solid-propellant gas generators allow residual propellants to reach plug nozzle for retro-rocket soft-landing on inflatable pontoons.

(*Above*) passengers from Pegasus intercontinental rocket transport board helicopter for swift transfer to city centre. (*Below*) Ithacus troop transport launched from nuclear carrier.

(Above) troops disembark from Ithacus rocket transport at their destination halfway across the world. *(Below)* after transfer from the interior, empty vehicle is taken by barge to a convenient coastal spaceport for reconditioning and relaunch.

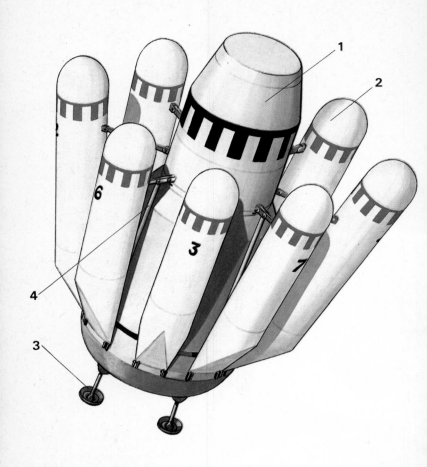

Pegasus variable-geometry entry configuration. *Key:* 1. Passenger compartment of re-usable single-stage vehicle; 2. Depleted fuel tanks hinged at base and actuated during re-entry to decrease velocity and provide manœuvrability *(8)*; 3. Landing legs extended for vertical touchdown on land *(4)*; 4. Actuation mechanism for rotating aft end of empty tanks to vary lift and drag during re-entry *(8)*.

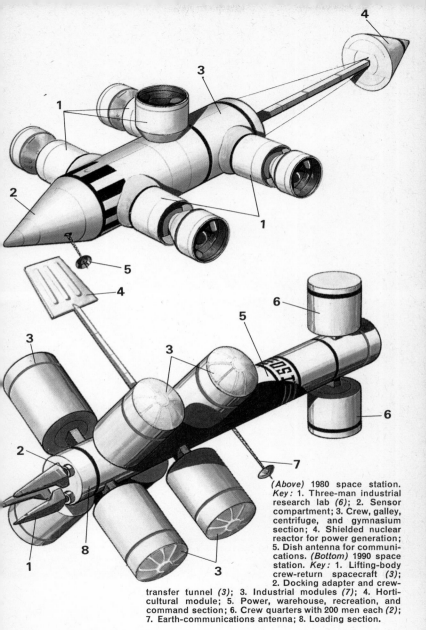

(Above) 1980 space station. *Key:* 1. Three-man industrial research lab *(6)*; 2. Sensor compartment; 3. Crew, galley, centrifuge, and gymnasium section; 4. Shielded nuclear reactor for power generation; 5. Dish antenna for communications. *(Bottom)* 1990 space station. *Key:* 1. Lifting-body crew-return spacecraft *(3)*; 2. Docking adapter and crew-transfer tunnel *(3)*; 3. Industrial modules *(7)*; 4. Horticultural module; 5. Power, warehouse, recreation, and command section; 6. Crew quarters with 200 men each *(2)*; 7. Earth-communications antenna; 8. Loading section.

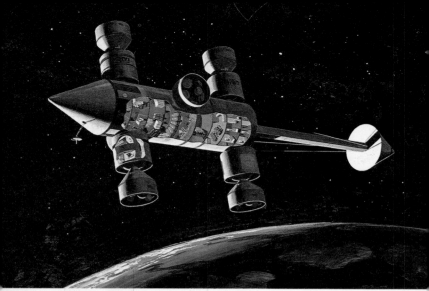

Artist's impression of advanced manned space stations detailed on page 83.
(Above) 1980s concept, *(below)* 1990s concept.

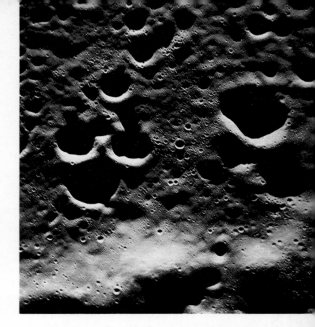

Moon exploration by man begins with Apollo. The lunar surface at about 3°S latitude and 160°W longitude on the Moon's far side, obtained by Apollo 8 astronauts Frank Borman, James Lovell, and William Anders. Also from Apollo 8, an area on the Moon's far side located at 10°S latitude and 160°E longitude within a large, unnamed crater, about 100 miles (161 km.) across. Note fresh rayed crater at upper right. Pictures are approximately 20 miles (32·2 km.) on a side.

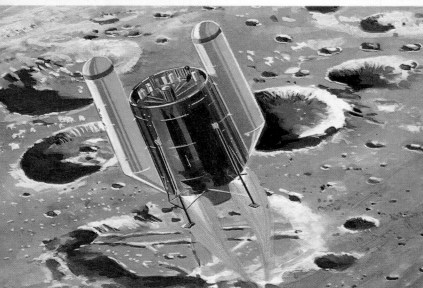

How re-usable **ROMBUS**-type launch vehicles can be applied to construction of a temporary lunar base (Project Selena). *(Above)* vehicle *en route* for the Moon is refuelled in Earth-orbit; and *(below)* soft-lands on the Moon with lunar base components.

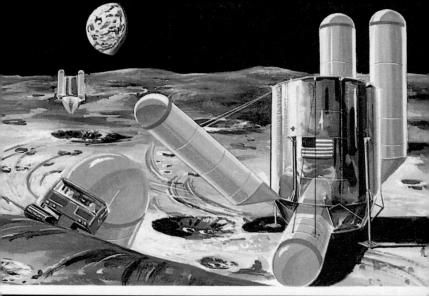

(*Above*) pressurized moon-tractor hauls hydrogen tanks adapted for human habitation to assembly site. (*Below*) the lunar base ready for occupation.

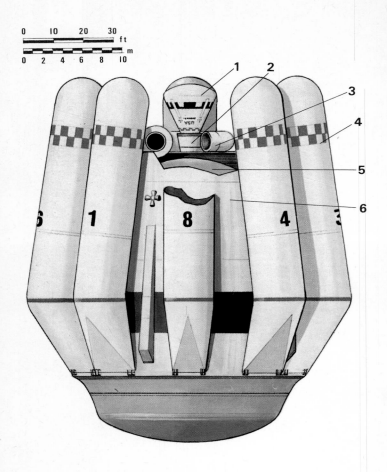

ROMBUS configuration for a manned Mars mission (Project Deimos).
Key : 1. Six-man Mars landing capsule; 2. Pressurized tunnel; 3. Toroidal living compartment; 4. Liquid hydrogen tanks *(8)*; 5. Spherical liquid oxygen tank; 6. Booster centrebody.

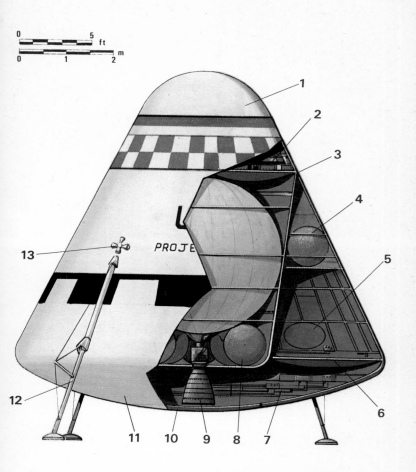

Project Deimos – Mars Landing Module. *Key:* 1. Earth-return capsule;
2. Command centre and pressurized tunnel; 3. Separation joint, for return
to Mars orbit; 4. Mars landing propellant tanks *(6)*; 5. Ground access hatch;
6. Mars-launch platform; 7. Payload and power supply equipment compartment;
8. Mars-launch propellant tank; 9. Landing and take-off rocket motor; 10. Jettisonable closure panel; 11. Mars-entry heat shield; 12. Extensible landing gear
(4); 13. Attitude-control system quads *(4)*.

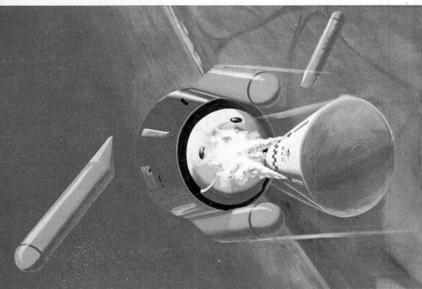

Mission to Mars (Project Deimos). *(Above)* hydrogen tanks jettison as ROMBUS spaceship accelerates from Earth-orbit. *(Below)* two hydrogen tanks jettison after retro-thrust into Mars orbit. Mars Landing Module separates from ROMBUS parent above the cratered deserts.

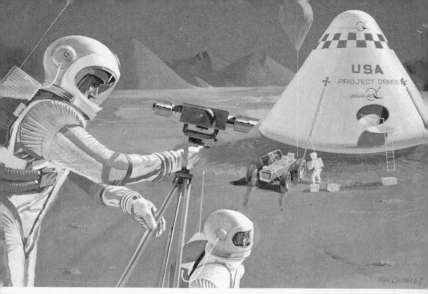

(Above) after soft-landing, astronauts begin exploration setting out research equipment and taking meteorological soundings. *(Below)* ascent stage of Mars Landing Module returns astronauts to ROMBUS parent in Martian orbit for return to Earth.

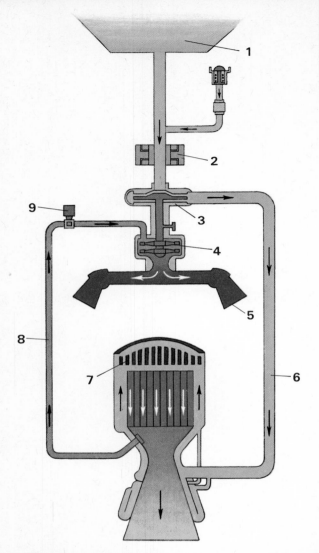

Nerva nuclear rocket engine: flow diagram. *Key:* 1. Liquid hydrogen tank; 2. Gimbal; 3. Pump; 4. Turbine; 5. Turbopump exhaust; 6. Nozzle coolant pipe (carries full hydrogen flow); 7. Shield; 8. Bleed to turbine (about 3 per cent of reactor efflux); 9. Turbine power control valve.

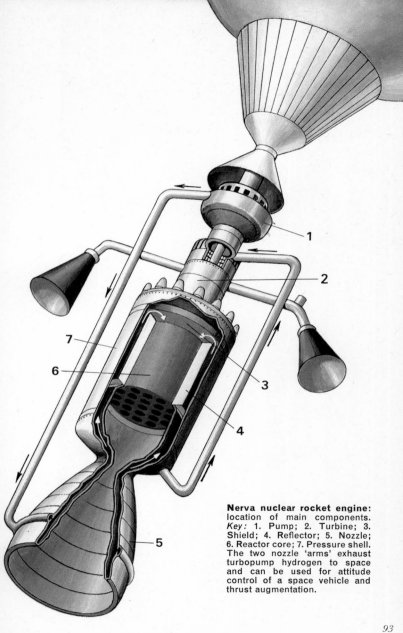

Nerva nuclear rocket engine: location of main components. *Key:* 1. Pump; 2. Turbine; 3. Shield; 4. Reflector; 5. Nozzle; 6. Reactor core; 7. Pressure shell. The two nozzle 'arms' exhaust turbopump hydrogen to space and can be used for attitude control of a space vehicle and thrust augmentation.

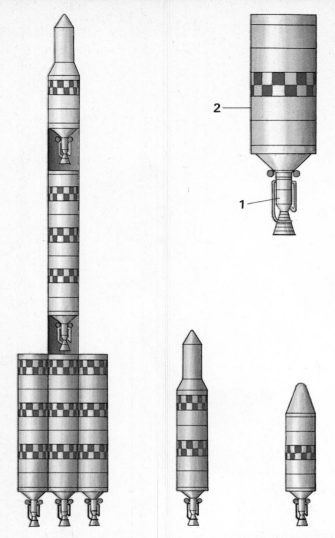

Nuclear-powered space vehicles can be assembled in Earth-orbit before beginning deep-space missions. Propulsion modules comprising Nerva 2 rocket engine 1 and 33 ft (10·05 m.) diameter hydrogen tank 2 can be used singly or in clusters. Various applications are illustrated. *(Bottom right)* an unmanned deep-space probe, *(centre)* a manned Mars fly-by, *(left)* a manned Mars landing. *(Top right)* a basic propulsion module of variable length and tank capacity. An optional rendezvous and docking structure can be fitted to the head section and a clustering structure fore and aft. Modules would be launched separately into orbit by Saturn-class chemical rockets or, alternatively, by a re-usable booster of the type discussed in this book.

Artist's impression of a nuclear rocket for a manned Mars mission. The huge vehicle, assembled in Earth-orbit, has five propulsion modules. Three parallel units are for injection into the transfer orbit to Mars, another is to brake the vehicle and inject it into an orbit around Mars, and the fifth is for the return to Earth. Chemical rockets would be carried for Mars landing and take-off. Total departure weight from Earth orbit is a massive 2,205,000 lb (1,000,000 kg.) allowing six to eight men to make the round trip in 450 days.

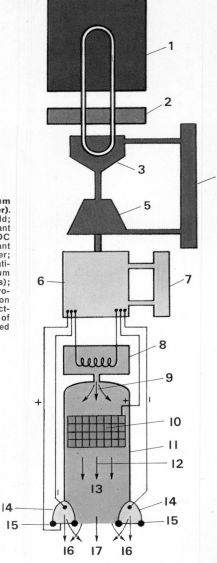

Working principle of cæsium ion rocket (after Stuhlinger). *Key :* 1. Nuclear reactor; 2. Shield; 3. Heat exchanger; 4. Radiant cooler; 5. Turbine; 6. AC and DC generating system; 7. Radiant cooler; 8. Cæsium vaporizer; 9. Cæsium vapour; 10. Hot platinum grid (which absorbs cæsium atoms and re-emits positive ions); 11. Thrust chamber; 12. Electrostatic field; 13. Ions; 14. Electron emitter; 15. Accelerating electrons; 16. Electrons (picked off of platinum grid); 17. Neutralized flow.

CHAPTER ONE

OUR WORLD FROM SPACE

Space research directed towards our own planet can bring rich rewards. The opportunities arise from the unique ability of artificial satellites to keep under regular observation vast areas of fertile land and deserts, the great oceans and polar regions, and weather changes affecting life and prosperity over the entire face of the world.

The technique depends on the ability of multi-band cameras and infra-red and microwave sensors to discriminate conditions on the Earth far beyond the ability of the human eye to see. Applications extend from geology, agriculture, forestry, hydrology, oceanography, and marine conservation to cartography, biology, and sociology. The results may be expected to benefit many branches of commerce and industry.

Few, if any, of these opportunities were realized when the space age began. When the first Tiros meteorological satellites started orbiting the Earth in the early 1960s the pictures they transmitted to ground stations showed cloud distribution over vast areas of the planet and sometimes familiar geographical outlines of land below, yet gave no clue that the Earth was inhabited. Then, one day, a picture was received of the Arctic on which appeared a straight line extending for hundreds of miles. It turned out to be the shadow of the vapour trail of a transpolar jet which the Sun had cast on the polar ice.

More evidence of human activity was forthcoming when a Tiros photograph revealed faint markings in the snows of northern Canada, later identified as the activities of a lumber company hauling huge quantities of logs ready for the spring thaw. From subsequent Tiros photographs the lumber companies were surprised to learn that they had been cutting forests in distinct chequered patterns.

It was not until man himself ventured into space that more definitive sightings were possible. When astronaut Cooper surveyed the Earth from his Mercury MA-9 capsule in May 1963, he reported seeing buildings, roads, and smoke from chimneys. At first space officials doubted the observations, and there was even talk of Cooper being hallucinated. (See *Manned Spacecraft*, by K. W. Gatland, Blandford Press, 1967, p. 158.) But later observations and colour photographs taken by astronauts from Gemini spacecraft using conventional cameras, provided certain proof of the ability to see artificial constructions on the Earth's surface, and even ships at sea, though orbiting in space at distances exceeding 100 miles (161 km.).

Not only did the pictures take in areas vastly more extensive than could be obtained from aircraft but features which went unnoticed from the ground and air took on fresh significance. Crustal faults were better identified, and certain land areas gave specialists new insight into possible mineral and oil deposits. An area of Texas where rain had fallen the day before was readily distinguishable from surrounding areas where it had not rained.

Meanwhile, reconnaissance satellites had been shown capable of returning photographs of airfields and launch sites in sufficient detail to make them meaningful, and important work had been accomplished with infra-red sensors in a bid to discriminate from orbit the 'exhaust signatures' of ballistic missiles. In developing the latter system, much attention had been given to conflicting sources of 'heat' emission, such as sunlight reflected from clouds.

The principle is basically this: all physical objects emit electro-magnetic radiation in proportion to their temperature. Infra-red occurs over a wide waveband, but broadly emissions can be divided into two regions, a near or 'hot', and a far or 'cold'. The hottest infra-red radiation (such as may be produced by a blast furnace, missile exhaust, or volcanoes can be recorded on special film, but in the far infra-red highly sensitive electronic techniques must be employed.

The new opportunities were clearly shown by observations made from manned and unmanned spacecraft in the 1960s. Different objects and conditions on Earth reflect distinctive amounts of heat and light, reflecting a different 'signature' to cameras and spectrometers.

Much of the basic research had been carried out with aircraft and important discoveries have sometimes come about quite unexpectedly. For example, scientists of the University of Michigan and the US Geological Survey, making aerial observations of volcanoes with infra-red sensors near Hawaii, found large tracts of water emerging from the coast that were as much as 12° F (−11° C) cooler than their surroundings.* What the sensor had discovered were huge quantities of fresh water running to waste in the ocean in a region where there is a distinct shortage.

The sensitivity of infra-red detectors is often hard for the layman to appreciate. It is now possible for soldiers to detect people in the jungle at night from the heat given off by their bodies – even to tell that an aircraft had taken off perhaps as long as an hour before simply by registering the cool shadow it has left behind on the runway.

Blast-furnaces, power stations, volcanoes, and forest fires are easy to detect from space; but the most discriminating work has to do with spotting ships and submarines from minute temperature differences in the sea. From this line of research is coming the ability to detect underground lakes and rivers in remote lands and measure the rainfall helpful to the conservation of fresh water. Infra-red sensors have also been fitted in satellites for sensing temperature changes in cloud layers to assist the complex process of weather forecasting.

One of the first efforts with Earth-resources satellites involved the preparation of a world geographical map far more accurate and complete than present maps made with the help of ground surveys and aircraft pictures of far smaller surface areas. More detailed maps could show the best routes for new systems of roads and railways or for irrigation channels. Maps can also be made of coral reefs close to the ocean surface and invisible to pilots of ships, contributing to safer navigation. In pictures taken by Gemini astronauts with the 70 mm. Hasselblad it was possible to see underwater geological formations and the effect of currents on the colour of the water.

How well the Earth's colours can be captured from 120 miles (193 km.) up is shown (page 18) in the Gemini 4 photographs of

* 'The all-seeing eye of the infra-red', *Electronic Age*, Radio Corporation of America.

the Ras Al Hadd area of Muscat and Oman; at the point can be seen the airport runways. At the base of the pediment are a number of oases where ground water has reached the surface. The furrowed area at the eastern extremities of the Rub Al Khali are long seif dunes of interest to the meteorologist.

Geologists found the colour photographs taken by Gemini astronauts contained important information. According to Dr Monem Abdel-Gawad at the North American Aviation Science Center, California, chromium-bearing rock formations in the north-eastern Egyptian desert near Gebel Abu Dahr were discovered to be four times as vast as ground exploration had previously indicated.

Dr Abdel-Gawad was among the first to emphasize the advantages of satellite observation to underdeveloped countries. It could save them years, if not decades, in finding the best areas for prospecting. Some minerals are known to be associated with certain classes of rock and can be located by rock colour and topographic form. Examples are chromium, iron, manganese, and phosphorites. Satellite photographs also showed that oil could be found in traps along transcurrent faults which correspond with major oilfields in the Gulf of Suez. Wherever in the world such formations occur, if they are free of dense vegetation or snow, they can be surveyed by means of satellite photography.

Another example occurred in Finland where a previously unknown fault structure was discovered on satellite photographs in a remote northern region. Part of this 'fault' was known to include a mining district rich in iron, magnesium, and chromium, and the geologists were led by the space pictures to make further explorations along the same fault line.

A picture obtained by Gemini 4 astronauts Schirra and Stafford showed a geological phenomenon called 'ring dykes' in the Aïr Mountains of the Niger Republic. Ring dykes – dark circular lava flows – are often pointers to the existence of valuable minerals, in this case tin, tungsten, and niobium, a rare metal.

Photographic surveys of this kind had previously been carried out from aircraft, but because of the lower altitude these covered only small areas compared with the enormous spread of territory visible from space. Nevertheless, airborne remote-sensing surveys have led to the discovery of major deposits of minerals. In Canada, for example, there have been such spectacular finds as the Manitoba nickel deposits of International Nickel, and the base metal discovery of Texas Gulf Sulphur in the Timmins, Ontario region.

Data acquired from space adds enormously to the ability to locate new sites of potential interest, not merely in the United States and Canada but throughout the world. Economic benefits to rich and poor countries alike, could be substantial. Similar possibilities apply to the discovery of new oilfields.

An idea of the amount of detail an astronaut can see from an orbiting spacecraft can be gauged from the photograph on page 22. Taken by Gemini 7 astronauts Borman and Lovell the picture shows part of the Kennedy Space Center on Merritt Island, Florida. Despite the cloud it is possible to see the two Saturn 5 launch pads joined to the Vehicle Assembly Building by the 3-mile (4·8 km.) long crawlerway; other launch pads can be seen along the coast as well as a whole complex of roads and causeways. The picture – obtained with a 35 mm. Zeiss Contarex fitted with a Questar telephoto lens – gives a small indication of the ability of reconnaissance satellites equipped with more specialized cameras to supply information of unlimited value.

When it was first suggested that photographs obtained from space could be used in urban planning, people were incredulous. Yet even the picture (page 22) obtained by a remote 70 mm. Maurer 220G aimed through the hatch window of Apollo 6 shows enough detail of the Dallas–Fort Worth area to be interesting on this account. The city of Denton can be seen in the upper centre of the picture at the conjunction of highways leading both to Fort Worth, below, and Dallas to the right. The highway system ringing Dallas is particularly prominent. Other identifiable features include reservoirs north of Fort Worth and Dallas, Carswell Air Force Base and General Dynamics plant at Fort Worth, the Greater Southwest International Airport, Love Field in Dallas, Ling-Temco-Vought Aerospace, and the Dallas Naval Air Station. This particular photo was taken on SO-121 high-resolution aerial Ektachrome with a camera setting of $f/5·6$ at 1/500th of a second.

Satellites can obtain photographic data required for cartography (mapping) on a global basis far more quickly than aircraft. For this purpose film cameras are superior to TV techniques in supplying data of metric quality, and the satellites must sweep low polar orbits. Just to cover the United States by aircraft at 30,000 ft (9,144 m.) would require some 100,000 stereo pairs, according to a study group of the National Academy of Sciences, whereas only 550 stereo pairs would be necessary using the broader range of vision of a satellite. This has considerable economic advantage. The cost of assembling 100,000 stereo pairs into controlled mosaics may be five to ten times the cost of the photography from aircraft. By comparison, the assembly of 550 stereo pairs is negligible.

Much could be learnt from direct photography using standard cameras and colour film. Some of the most significant observations were made by Gemini astronauts who could direct their cameras at interesting features as the Earth's vast panorama passed by.

The beauty of the Indian sub-continent and Ceylon as seen from Gemini 11 is strikingly recorded in the photograph on page 17. Millions of people are represented in this picture, and as Arthur Clarke has pointed out, their life depends on the distribution of certain white patches – the pre-Monsoon clouds. For the first time we are beginning to understand how the weather system works. Much valuable information is contained about the meteorological conditions over such an enormous area as the sub-continent and the adjacent Arabian Sea to the left and the Bay of Bengal to the right. The climatic difference along the divide of Western Ghats is clearly seen. The lush green jungle is to the west and the semi-arid browns are to the east.

Other meteorological conditions appear in the Gemini 5 photograph (page 18) which shows a very well developed vortex caused by windshear at the coastal prominence of Ras Rhir in Morocco. The picture clearly shows the 'eye' and the rotational effects on the periphery. NASA points to this as being a classic example of the kind of meteorological data which can result from manned spaceflight. It would be difficult, indeed, to provide a machine with the knowledge and intelligence to select and photograph phenomena of greatest value.

The study of vortices is of particular importance to the meteorologist as the ultimate vortex can be destructive tornados, hurricanes, and typhoons. A rare spectacle awaited Gemini astronauts when they first glimpsed the mile-high island of Guadalupe off the coast of Mexico. A photograph clearly shows how the island interrupts the orderly flow of winds and creates a bowed shockwave effect in the clouds to windward and two vortices which have developed to the lee of the island.

Earth's ever-changing cloud cover was never properly observed until cameras could be operated in space. The picture on page 18 was taken by a remote 70 mm. Maurer camera aimed through the hatch window of the unmanned Apollo 6 spacecraft on 4 April 1968. It shows the east coast of the United States between Savannah and Brunswick, Georgia, from an altitude of 100 nautical miles (185 km.). Over the Atlantic can be seen the vapour trails of jet aircraft.

Forces of wind and sea are clearly demonstrated in a photograph (page 23) of south-west Africa taken from an altitude of 200 miles (322 km.). The area is the Namib Desert along the Skeleton Coast which derives its name from many wrecks which littered the shore when galleons used this route from Western Europe to the riches of Asia 500 years ago. This is one of the world's driest areas. The seif-type dunes stretch over 100 miles (161 km) across the southern region; but as the prevailing winds carry the sand into the Atlantic Ocean, the strong Benguela Current causes the northward waterborne migration of sands and the formation of the three very large sand hooks. The port of Walvis Bay is situated on the lee side of the northernmost hook which extends for 50 miles (80 km.).

At last it became possible to view the Earth's weather systems on a massive scale. The picture of the Earth globe in colour (page 17) was obtained by television from the Advanced Technology Satellite-3 in geo-stationary orbit at 47 W longitude over Brazil. It was this same multi-purpose satellite that relayed coverage of the Mexico Olympiad to Europe in October 1968.

Four continents – parts of North and South America, Africa, and Europe, and the Greenland ice-cap – can be seen while the Antarctic continent is blanketed by cloud. The major weather system over the central United States, stretching from the Great Lakes to Mexico, represents a cold front moving eastwards. A tropical storm can be seen (bottom centre) with a cold front extending into Argentina.

The picture was built up from electronic signals in red, green, and blue and recorded on a composite colour negative at the ground station.

Apart from their economic benefits, space satellites can do much to safeguard life and property on Earth. Advanced warning of destructive storms, hurricanes, and typhoons, can be given immediately to ground stations allowing evacuation of coastal areas; rough sea conditions can be monitored either directly or in conjunction with radio-equipped buoys located in strategic areas. Turbulent sea conditions, according to New York University, may be indicated by radar backscatter which bears a strong relationship to surface wind, and thus to the size of ocean waves. Measurement of the 'backscatter' by a low-power microwave sensor, may make it possible to predict which ocean areas will have high waves.

Much attention is being devoted to the tracking of hurricanes and typhoons so that shipping and coastal areas can be forewarned of their approach. Nimbus II photographed and tracked 17 typhoons, 9 hurricanes and 9 tropical storms.

Not long ago there was a first-class example of the way in which satellites bring emergency relief. Torrential rains had filled the Nazas River basin in Mexico as Hurricane Naomi swept in from the sea. The extensive flooding caused potentially dangerous water pressures to build up behind the newly completed Lazaro Cardenas Dam. The Mexican authorities were faced with a dilemma. If the rains continued they would be forced to open the dam, flooding the city of Gomez Palacios and losing the water needed for the region's agricultural programme. If the dam remained closed, there was grave danger that it would burst and flood not only Gomez Palacios but the city of Torreon as well.

The day was saved when television pictures transmitted by the ESSA 6 weather satellite indicated that the storm had run its course. Acting on this information, the authorities kept the dam closed, saving two cities and assuring an abundant water supply for future use in irrigation.

Hurricanes and typhoons draw their energy from the heat of tropical oceans. Winds form a vortex of storm clouds extending for thousands of feet into the atmosphere; barometric pressure drops in the centre and the whole system becomes a gigantic heat pump, sucking warmth from the sea surface. Thanks to weather satellites we are beginning to see how hurricanes behave. Nimbus II gave meteorologists their first complete view of the life and death cycle when Hurricane Alma, born in the Caribbean in June 1966, was photographed during its entire lifespan of seven days until it petered out south of Newfoundland.

In related experiments satellite data has been used in attempts to break up hurricanes in their early stages of formation by seeding them with silver iodide. If enough of the chemical is injected, the ice crystals produced within the core of the hurricane will lower the temperature sufficient to cause it to break up.

Experiments of this kind have been made jointly by the US Navy and the Environmental Science Services Administration in a programme called Stormfury in an attempt to reduce the menace of hurricanes which, each year, cause millions of dollars' worth of damage and many deaths.

Infra-red sensing from space can be used to measure the temperature of volcanoes and ultimately may provide advance warning of volcanic eruptions. Infra-red measurements of the newly formed volcanic island of Surtsey, near Iceland, by the US weather satellite Nimbus II gave geologists their first detailed temperature profile of the molten material exuded from the Earth's interior. Gemini photographs led scientists to discover a geological fault in Peru which could present a potential earthquake hazard.

Clouds of migrating locusts, detectable from aircraft, may also be seen from satellites, providing another form of advance warning.

In agriculture the prospects for space observation are no less promising. Multi-band cameras can obtain pictures of the Earth in false colours, revealing features that the eye cannot register. It is similar to the ability of someone who is colour-blind being able to see through camouflage, which led to experiments with filters that blocked out various parts of the colour spectrum. Different species of trees and crops reflect light in various bands of the visible and infra-red ranges in different degrees, and multi-spectral sensors, similar to TV cameras, can obtain false colour pictures in which it is possible to distinguish oats from barley, diseased from healthy crops, and polluted water from clean. Again, basic research is being conducted with aircraft, but there seems no reason why a mixture of satellites and aircraft should not achieve a practical surveillance system for world-wide forestry and agriculture applications, leading to increased food production and more effective control of plant diseases and pests. For example, the cost of preparing a natural forest inventory by conventional means in the United States alone has been put at almost $11 million. Space sensing could reduce this cost dramatically while the use of remote sensors in a satellite – providing an advance warning system for forest fires – should allow an 8 per cent reduction in the area of forests damaged or destroyed. At present forest fires cost the United States alone an estimated $4,000 million per year.

The ability of space cameras to reveal information of agricultural interest is shown on page 19. This is the Edwards Plateau area of Texas and includes the cities of Odessa, Midland, and Big Spring on the right just out of view on this reproduction. The fingers of darker green are the effect of a rainstorm the previous evening. The area is semi-arid and vegetation has quickly demonstrated its vigour. The more fertile regions of the upper Concho and its tributaries are also apparent.

Much attention is being paid to extending the spectral range of cameras, as already indicated, so that the vigour of crops can be determined. Again, basic research has been performed from aircraft. A typical picture in which spectral values have been changed shows healthy fields of potatoes in red, and those afflicted by blight in black (page 20).

As different objects reflect distinctive amounts of heat or light, experimental data from a whole range of sensors can be fed into a computer to produce a map of agricultural distribution. A block of 'O's signifies a field of oats, an adjacent block of 'W's wheat, 'C's corn, and so on. This immediately suggests the possibility of assessing the world's agricultural resources and estimating the yield in different areas.

Another fruitful area for space-sensing is hydrology, where it is important to assess ground moisture content, the rate of evaporation from reservoirs and lakes, and run-off to be expected from snow-clad mountains in the spring. Assessments of this kind may lead to improved water conservation in traditional drought areas, and even to the accurate forecasting of flood or drought conditions. It may even be possible to discriminate between clean and chemically, or biologically contaminated water by contrasts in water colour.

The potential use of space photography in the observation of the causes and distribution of water pollutants is clearly demonstrated in photographs. A photograph of the Texas-Louisiana Gulf Coast shows Houston, including the Manned Spacecraft Center, the Harris County Domed Stadium, the Houston Ship Channel, and other well-known features. But NASA scientists were more impressed by the wealth of detail on waterborne sediments in the bays, and their movement through such passes as Bolivar Roads, Sabine Pass, and Calcasieu Pass. The movement of currents in the Gulf of Mexico is also apparent. From this the oceanographer can extract much useful information, for example, about the movement and distribution of larval shrimp, important to the economy of the area.

Sensitive infra-red sensors may actually help to locate hidden water resources, such as underground springs and lakes, from minute variations in ground temperature.

Several countries meet 'at the roof of the world' on page 24. The photograph includes Sinkiang Province in China, parts of India, Pakistan, Kashmir, Afghanistan, and Tadzhik in the USSR. The Korakoran Range of the Himalayas is snow covered above 20,000 ft (6,096 m.); Mt Godwin-Austen (K-2), the world's second highest peak at 28,250 ft (8,616 m.), is near the left edge. The Indus River flows in the lower portion of the photograph. The upper left shows the Takla Makin basin. Taken at the time of minimum snow cover, space photography similar to this Gemini 5 photograph can provide data on water yields from snowfields or remote and poorly explored mountain ranges.

Regular photography of coastal areas should contribute much to our knowledge of sea erosion and the silting of estuaries. Sedimentation in coastal waters was clearly apparent by colour contrast in Gemini photographs. It should therefore be possible to study many problems associated with erosion and sedimentation, including the formation and movement of shoals and sandbars in rivers.

Air pollution may also be monitored from space-satellites allowing scientists to pin-point peaks of contamination, wind drift, and relationships with local weather patterns.

Many of the space pictures turned up information of interest about the oceans and inshore currents especially near the estuaries of great rivers.

Even more remarkable is the photograph (page 24) of the Great Bahama Banks obtained from Gemini 5 for it provides information which is hidden to the surface observer. Apart from small land areas of Great Exuma Island, Cat Island, and Long Island, many features seen in this picture are beneath the sea. 'Along the edge of the Tongue of the Ocean, over a mile deep, we see canyons cut in the coral banks. Exuma Sound, at the centre of the photograph, drops abruptly from rocks awash to a depth of 8,000 ft (2,438 m.).'

Photography and infra-red sensing of the oceans may bring important economic rewards. The fishing industry could benefit considerably from the increasing attention now being given to currents and temperature patterns in the ocean which tend to attract large shoals of fish. Early satellite observations showed it was possible to photograph with infra-red cameras the Gulf Stream as it flows from the eastern seaboard of the United States north-eastward across the Atlantic. At the same time heat given off by the warm current was measured by radiometers aboard satellites which gave additional information on the location and movement of huge ocean masses of interest to oceanographers, meteorologists, and the fishing and shipping industries.

One of the first space experiments for guiding fishing-boats to big catches was made over the Gulf of Guinea, off the west coast of Africa. The project, financed by NASA, depended on ESSA weather satellites photographing 'black water' areas in the Gulf forming a corridor between warm and cool ocean masses, difficult to locate at sea, where schools of tuna fish abound. Working with the American weather satellites was the oceanographic vessel, *Undaunted*, which was fitted with Automatic Picture Transmission equipment for receiving satellite pictures. Photographs were obtained of the surrounding ocean in visible light, whilst at night they were transmitted in infra-red. It had been anticipated that the constantly shifting boundary between masses of warm and cool water would show up on the satellite pictures, particularly in the infra-red transmissions at night, and indeed this proved to be the case.

Heat-sensing of the oceans is not the only avenue of fisheries research. The different spectral response due to the presence of plankton in the water can also be important for tracing life patterns in the sea and feeding-grounds for fish, while the US Bureau of Commercial Fisheries has even devoted attention to detecting schools of fish through an oily residue they leave behind on the ocean's surface.

Another important area of oceanographic research depends on photographing ice conditions in the Arctic and Antarctic. Particularly in the Northern Hemisphere, there are waterways which are frozen for large parts of the year. As these are often trade routes for merchant shipping there is economic advantage in keeping these areas under direct surveillance so that the ice situation can be rapidly assessed. Because of the enormous distances involved it is difficult and expensive to maintain an effective ice patrol solely with aircraft. Increasingly, it is being found that the overall view obtainable from satellites is both the most effective and cheapest method of ice reconnaissance. By studying satellite photographs of the Gulf of Bothnia on the Baltic coast, Finnish scientists have been able to rapidly assess the ice situation and dispatch breakers to open up the sea lanes at precisely the right time. Space photography has also become a valuable aid in opening up the St Lawrence Seaway to shipping with the onset of spring.

Similar benefits apply in the Soviet Union where satellite pictures have been used from the beginning to enable fishing and merchant vessels to select the best possible routes.

Remote Sensing Applications from Satellites

THE EARTH

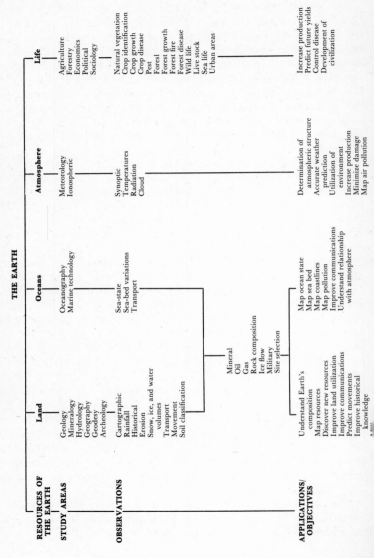

	Land	Oceans	Atmosphere	Life
RESOURCES OF THE EARTH				
STUDY AREAS	Geology Mineralogy Hydrology Geography Geodesy Archeology	Oceanography Marine technology	Meteorology Ionospheric	Agriculture Forestry Economics Political Sociology
OBSERVATIONS	Cartographic Rainfall Historical Erosion Snow, ice, and water volumes Transport Movement Soil classification Mineral Oil Gas Rock composition Ice flow Military Site selection	Sea-state Sea-bed variations Transport	Synoptic Temperatures Radiation Cloud	Natural vegetation Crop identification Crop growth Crop disease Pest Forest Forest growth Forest fire Forest disease Wild life Live stock Sea life Urban areas
APPLICATIONS/ OBJECTIVES	Understand Earth's composition Map resources Discover new resources Improve land utilization Improve communications Predict movements Improve historical knowledge	Map ocean state Map sea bed Map coastlines Map pollution Improve communications Understand relationship with atmosphere	Determination of atmospheric structure Accurate weather prediction Utilization of environment Increase production Minimize damage Map air pollution	Increase production Predict future yields Control disease Development of civilization

In dealing with marine aspects of Earth resources survey, it is impossible to separate space observations from researches carried out on and below the ocean surface. To meet the protein needs of the world population in the 1980s new effort in marine technology will be required to raise the productivity of the fishing industry. Two-thirds of the world's population are in developing countries, and population doubles in most of them in 18 to 27 years.

Probing coastal areas from the air and space can do much towards exploiting untapped mineral and oil resources. Altogether, the following areas were considered important by the Marine Sciences Council: (*a*) delineation of the migration and movement patterns of major commercial fish stocks; (*b*) fishery exploration in currently unexploited areas; (*c*) acquisition of data relating to fish distribution to environmental factors as a basis for providing fishery prediction services; (*d*) preparation of small-scale topographic, geological, magnetic, and gravity maps of the continental shelf and slope to identify mineral and fuel resources areas – oil and gas; (*e*) preparation of geophysical and topographic maps of selected areas of the deep ocean floor; (*f*) coring and drilling surveys of the continental margin and deep ocean floor in selected areas; (*g*) facilitating data exchanges; (*h*) determination of the origin and dynamics of ocean current systems; (*i*) investigations of heat exchange and transport, air-sea interactions, and air-mass modification; (*j*) studies of storm genesis propagation and waves.

While much of the effort depends on passive sensing techniques, satellites can also work directly in conjunction with other devices on the Earth, in the oceans, or in the atmosphere. For example, satellites can be used to collect information from free-floating buoys adrift in the oceans. Within the buoys are electronic devices obtaining data on currents, ocean depths, temperatures and salinity, and a telemetry transmitter. The satellite will interrogate the buoys once or twice a day, store their data, and relay these at an appropriate time to a ground receiving station.

From this research may come the ability to locate turbulent upwellings of nutrients along the perimeters of major current streams, providing food for shoals of fish.

Ten major areas for study were proposed using a combination

of oceanographic ships, ocean buoys, aircraft, and spacecraft: (1) sea state and sea-level measurement; (2) thermal measurements of the sea surface; (3) location and mapping of surface ocean currents; (4) sea ice measurement and location and classification of icebergs; (5) river discharge and delta studies; (6) delineation of shorelines, shoals, and sea bottom contours, and elimination of 'doubtful' shoals in the high seas; (7) detection and measurement of biota; (8) sea slope measurements; (9) observations of air-sea interaction phenomena; (10) detection of upwelling zones.

How these various opportunities may be exploited in the future by large space observatories will be discussed in Chapter Eight.

CHAPTER TWO

LABORATORIES IN ORBIT

Despite the excellent results obtained by unmanned satellites during the first space decade, observations by astronauts from orbit and their unique ability to deal with the unexpected, made it certain that man would find an important role in space. At last the ideas of the astronautical pioneers – Tsiolkovsky, Oberth, 'Noordung', and von Pirquet began to bear fruit in space-station technology. The first manned systems, however, were to be far from the giant rigid platforms envisaged in the 1920s and 1930s. It was found more practical to assemble clusters of laboratory modules in orbit. Not only did this eliminate the need for astronauts to perform elaborate assembly tasks outside their craft but it allowed different laboratory modules to rendezvous with the parent as they were needed.

Advances in automation made it possible for equipment to be left operating in orbit, or switched off as desired, while the laboratory modules received periodic visits from astronauts for specialized experiments or the repair and replacement of expensive equipment. A complex of this kind orbiting some 200 miles (322 km.) above the Earth has particular value in meteorology, ice reconnaissance, storm warning, Earth resources survey, and astronomy. It can also become a data reception centre for other spacecraft, manned and unmanned, operating at altitudes out to synchronous orbit at 22,300 miles (35,880 km.). Another part of its function would be the rescue of astronauts who found themselves in difficulty. Small space taxis would be available for transferring astronauts between laboratory modules of the orbiting complex where these were not physically docked with the parent.

A strong indication of Soviet intentions was the automatic rendezvous and docking between two pairs of unmanned Cosmos satellites in 1967–68 (page 26). These vehicles were similar to the Soyuz (Union) 1 spacecraft in which Engineer-Colonel Vladimir Komarov perished when the parachute lines of the re-entry capsule tangled during his return from orbit on 24 April 1967.

The basic philosophy behind the docking experiments had been outlined in an historic speech by the late Yuri Gagarin in 1963 before the International Astronautical Federation in Paris.

Gagarin began by saying that a flight to the Moon would require a space vehicle weighing several tens of tonnes; it was no secret that such large rockets were not yet available. The problem could be solved in different ways, and the alternatives were being studied both in the United States and in his own country. One technique, Gagarin emphasized, involved the assembly of parts of spaceships in near-orbit. Once in orbit the components could be collected together, joined up, and supplied with propellant. The interplanetary flight could then begin.

Gagarin went on to say that the problems associated with such procedures were very complex and they required complicated systems of communication and radar and optical observation. When equipment was near the limits of its resolving powers and capability, it would be necessary for man to take a direct hand to control the approach of space vehicles. 'In this connection,' he said, 'we carried out group flights such as those by Nikolayaev and Popovich, and Tereshkova and Bykovsky, when two Vostok spacecraft were put into very close orbits with separation distances down to 4 to 2·5 miles (6·5 to 4 km.).' Such small distances, Gagarin continued, would require no great consumption of propellant in order to make an approach.

On future spaceflights, it would be necessary to send crews into orbit in multi-seat craft in order to obtain more detailed experience of the tasks to be given to cosmonauts. Clearly, scientists would also go into space so that further study could be made. As one man could not be expected to pilot a spaceship and make a wide range of scientific research, there would have to be changes in the basic techniques of spaceflight 'since at present only very healthy and physically prepared people can withstand the accelerations and decelerations of launching and re-entry'.

Gagarin's words have since been fully borne out by events. The first scientist and a medical doctor went into orbit a year later aboard Voskhod 1; orbital rendezvous and docking (with emphasis on man-monitored automatic systems) has been demon-

strated, and effort has been devoted to reducing the high-*g* forces
endured by cosmonauts.

In the Soviet docking experiments performed with similar
Cosmos vehicles, one spacecraft remained passive in a fixed orbit
while the other carried out the necessary manœuvres. After the
active craft had been brought within a certain distance of its
target by ground or pilot control, each vehicle began an active
search for the other using a radio-location technique; then, with
the aid of on-board computers, the active craft automatically
responded by changing its velocity according to the most economical approach path. When it had arrived within 984 to 1,312 ft
(300 to 400 m.) of its objective, the final approach was made at
a low relative velocity with both craft properly aligned for docking
nose to nose. The docking probe on the active vehicle entered the
receptor of the target and there was an immediate mechanical
linkage including the interconnection of electrical circuits.

The same docking procedure can apply to the assembly of a
large rocket module to a spacecraft; to space station assembly; to
the transfer of men and supplies to a space station by smaller 'ferry'
vehicles; and to the rescue of cosmonauts who may be stranded in
Earth orbit.

Two events at the end of 1968 were to reveal the objectives in
more detail. After Colonel (now Major-General) Georgy Beregovy
had performed rendezvous experiments in Soyuz 3 with a similar
unmanned spacecraft, it was revealed that the vehicle comprised
three modules (page 27). In the extreme nose was a spherical
orbital compartment containing a block of equipment for scientific
experiments, a rest compartment, and the entrance hatch.
Included in the equipment block were the life-support system,
scientific apparatus, food, a medical kit, and a 'washstand'.
Adjoining this section – with an interconnecting hatch – was the
cosmonaut's re-entry module with flight controls, and aft of that
the equipment module with two liquid-propellant 882-lb (400-
kg.)-thrust rocket engines – one a back-up system – for mid-course
manœuvres and retro-fire. Two extensible wing-like solar panels
had 150 ft² (14 m.²) area and there were four TV cameras, two
of them being outside to give the crew a visual presentation of the
docking procedure.

The multi-man Soyuz spacecraft – in effect a miniature manned space laboratory – had a combined habitable volume of about 317·8 ft³ (9 m.³). A two-gas atmosphere of oxygen/nitrogen was maintained at sea-level pressure.

Work tasks of these vehicles were officially stated to be:

(a) All-round study of the Earth and its atmosphere with the object of solving problems in radio-physics, geophysics, and space navigation;

(b) Study of problems involved in using the near-Earth environment (high vacuum, weightlessness and radiation) for scientific and practical purposes; and

(c) Study of the Sun, stars, planets, and their moons.

The Soyuz vehicles which were highly manœuvrable for rendezvous with other spacecraft, were stated to be 'of major importance for setting up research stations in orbit, consisting of several autonomous elements delivered into orbit'.

What *Tass* described as the world's first experimental space station was established for 4 hr. 35 min. on 16 January 1969 when two manned spacecraft, Soyuz 4 and 5, were successfully docked in Earth orbit. Each craft had a spherical orbital compartment in addition to the re-entry module for scientific experiments giving a combined habitable volume of 635·7 ft³ (18 m.³). The station's orbit ranged between 129·7 and 155 miles (209 to 250 km.) inclined at 51°40′ to the equator.

Soyuz 5, which became the passive vehicle during rendezvous and docking, had three cosmonauts: command pilot Lieutenant-Colonel Boris Volynov; flight engineer Alexei Yeliseyev, and research engineer Lieutenant-Colonel Yevgeny Khrunov. The active craft Soyuz 4 was launched with a single occupant, command pilot Lieutenant-Colonel Vladimir Shatolov, who took over manual control when the distance between the two vehicles was down to 328 ft (100 m.). The subsequent nose-to-nose docking achieved mechanical and electrical interconnection, and telephone communications were immediately established between all four habitable compartments of the composite station.

During the thirty-fifth orbit (of Soyuz 4) Soyuz 5 cosmonauts Khrunov and Yeliseyev donned spacesuits, the orbital compartments of both craft were sealed and depressurized, and the two men emerged through a hatch into outer space. Their work outside the craft included installation and dismantling of ciné-camera supports, handrails and television equipment. The men also performed various movements simulating more complicated assembly tasks. After about an hour, they entered the hatch of Soyuz 4 and, when the orbital compartment had been repressurized, removed their suits. The interconnecting hatch to the command module was then opened and they took up new working places beside cosmonaut Shatalov.

When the docking exercise was completed the craft were separated and their re-entry modules safely recovered. Thus ended the first transfer of cosmonauts from one spacecraft to another in orbit, with three men returning in the vehicle that originally had contained only one. Such an experiment was important, said Yeliseyev, 'for assembling heavier orbital stations in space in the not too distant future, for examining their exteriors and for different repair and assembly tasks outside the station'. *Tass* made the point that the mission had created 'preconditions for implementing such operations in space as the replacement of crews of long-duration orbital stations and the rescue of spacecraft crews under emergency conditions'.

Academician Mstislav Keldysh, president of the USSR Academy of Sciences, linked the experiment with the broad objectives of Soviet space effort which included 'the investigation of near-Earth space and planets; the assembly of big, constantly operating orbital stations; interplanetary flights, and advances in radio, television and other branches of science and technology'. In his opinion, the time when permanent large-size orbital stations would start operating was 'years and not decades away'.

Another important aspect of Soyuz, necessary for the orbiting of scientists and others who had not previously trained as jet-pilots, were the provisions made to reduce *g*-loading during re-entry. First the craft was correctly orientated for retro-fire and the liquid-propellant engine in the equipment module fired for 145 sec. (in the case of Soyuz 3).

After separation the cone-shaped re-entry module was able to make a semi-ballistic re-entry in which decelerative forces were limited to 3–4 g instead of the 8–10 g previously experienced using a technique of controlled aerodynamic braking. The drogue parachute deployed at 5·6 miles (9 km.) altitude followed by the main parachute and final touch-down was softened by solid retro-rockets fired when the craft was only 3·28 ft (1 m.) from the ground.

Aerodynamic lift – obtained by offsetting the capsule's centre of gravity and pitching the vehicle's heat shield up, down, or sideways to produce appropriate deflection forces – was also demonstrated by the unmanned circumlunar spacecraft Zond 6.

The manœuvre was achieved first by entering a 6·2-mile (9·98 km.) wide re-entry corridor some 28 miles (45 km.) above the Earth, during which speed was reduced from 7 miles/sec. (11·2 km./sec.) to 4·7 miles/sec. (7·6 km./sec.). Then, the capsule was orientated to create maximum lift and made to perform an aerodynamic skip out of the atmosphere, after which it made a second re-entry for further aerodynamic braking and parachute recovery.

It is well to recall that the American spacecraft Gemini and Apollo were also designed to achieve aerodynamic lift rather than purely ballistic flight, and some of the accuracies obtained in returning to appointed landing places were quite remarkable. (See *Manned Spacecraft*, by K. W. Gatland, Blandford Press, 1967, pp. 174–176.)

In the United States the principles of space-station technology were worked out with hardware originally developed for the Apollo lunar mission.

To produce the orbital workshop of the Apollo Applications Programme, McDonnell-Douglas engineers began by modifying the S-IVB stage of the Saturn 1B launch vehicle. The primary aim was to ensure that the rocket stage could be speedily adapted in orbit for astronaut habitation. In this project the empty liquid hydrogen tank is transformed into two-storey accommodation as large as a three-bedroomed house. Over 21 ft (6·4 m.) deep, the tank provides a total volume of about 10,000 ft³ (283·17 m.³) divided by a lightweight metal grating. One section serves as living quarters and the other as work space for various experiments.

Before the S-IVB stage is lifted into orbit by the Saturn 1B, the manufacturer installs a multiple airlock and docking adapter at the forward end to provide air and other life-support essentials. For the initial workshop mission supplies were considered sufficient to provide a shirt-sleeve environment inside the tank section for 30 days.

A load-bearing truss structure supports the compartmented tunnel assembly of the airlock and multiple docking adapter. Including the structural transition section the airlock is 16 ft (4·87 m.) long, being fixed to the stage at the same four attachment points as used for the lunar module in the standard Apollo Earth-orbital test programme.

Four viewing ports, spaced approximately 90° apart, are provided in the transition section as are most of the airlock controls. The 65 in. (165 cm.) diameter tunnel assembly includes two internal bulkheads with hatches and a flexible pressure-tight assembly which is connected to the liquid hydrogen tank of the S-IVB stage. The tunnel allows visiting astronauts to transfer directly from the docked Apollo within the pressurized environment of the orbital assembly. The airlock compartment also contains a Gemini hatch in the tunnel wall which allows an astronaut, protected by his spacesuit, to perform extra-vehicular activity (EVA) while retaining full pressurization in the workshop cluster. The airlock compartment, in fact, is big enough to accommodate two astronauts in pressurized suits with portable life-support equipment.

The multiple docking adapter is a cylindrical pressurized vessel 17 ft 2 in. (5·2 m.) long and 12 ft (3·66 m.) in diameter at its widest point. It is attached to the airlock by a structural transition section. As can be seen in the drawing (page 28) the forward end tapers and includes an axial docking port. Four additional docking ports are equally spaced on the cylindrical section at right angles to the axis. Three of these radial ports are configured for Apollo CSM docking and the other for docking of the Apollo Telescope Mount (ATM).

To facilitate access a grid floor, normal to the longitudinal axis, is located approximately 23 in. (58·4 cm.) below the centre-lines of the radial docking ports. Four flat grid walls, parallel to the axis, are mounted between the structural transition section and the grid floor. There is about 1,500 ft³ (42·5 m.³) available for stowage of equipment and supplies during launch and orbital flight.

Modifications to the S-IVB tank interior, simplifying subsequent astronaut activity in orbit, were made to rocket stages on the production line. Fixed to the hydrogen tank wall were threaded studs to serve as attachment points for floors, handholds for rails on which equipment could be mounted if the stage was used as a 'workshop'; a stage 'passivation' system was developd that would assure the shutdown of unwanted electrical circuits, dumping of unused hydraulic fluids and pneumatic gases and complete ventilation of the hydrogen tank before the crewmen enter. A quick-opening hatch for easy access through the manhole at the top of the hydrogen tank was also embodied, replacing a standard manhole cover held in place by 72 bolts. Finally, a fire-resistant aluminium foil liner, was installed over the hydrogen tank's plastic foam insulation and a 'meteoroid bumper' installed on the outside of the stage. The shield of 0·025 in. (0·063 cm.) thick aluminium sheeting during the launch phase is held against the stage's liquid hydrogen tank. Once in orbit it is deployed by swing-links operated by torsion springs and held 5 in. (12·7 cm.) from the tank wall.

Adaptation of the S-IVB stage in orbit begins after three astronauts have arrived in an Apollo spacecraft (command and service modules) and docked with it. The men leave their spacecraft through the interconnecting tunnel, enter the airlock, and prepare to activate the inbuilt systems. After the last traces of propellant have been vented from the rocket, they open the sealed hatch in the hydrogen tank and climb into the interior to begin the conversion which will take several days.

First, the astronauts install partitions to make separate 'rooms' inside the huge cylinder. To help them control their movements in the absence of gravity, handholds, rails, and nets are fixed to the tank walls.

The assembled workshop is shown on page 30. Crew quarters are located in the aft end of the tank, a common floor separating these from a large laboratory area above. Pre-installed partitions divide the crew compartments, food and waste management compartments and a work area. A cloth ceiling installed adjacent to the common bulkhead of the liquid oxygen/liquid hydrogen tank serves as a reference surface for the astronauts and also reflects the maximum amount of light.

Compartments for food and waste management each having 30 ft² (2·79 m.²) of floor area are sealed with aluminium sheeting and have folding doors to restrict the circulation of odours and particles. The largest sleeping compartment has a floor area of 67 ft² (6·22 m.²) and the other 70 ft² (6·50 m.²). Floor area of the work compartment is 181 ft² (15·8 m.²).

Comfortable living conditions are ensured by a thermal control and ventilation system with a temperature range of 60 to 90° F. A safe two-gas oxygen-nitrogen atmosphere is maintained with an internal pressure of 5 to 6 p.s.i. Fans circulate the air and help to maintain a stable temperature.

Last to be brought into the tank are equipment and supplies stored during launch in the multiple docking adapter. The pre-installed electrical power distribution system connects the work-shop living and laboratory quarters with power sources in the airlock and solar cell assemblies. Lights are installed by the astronauts and may be moved about at their discretion.

The workshop has a 'caution and warning' system comprising sensors and an indicator/controller panel to alert the crew to dangerous conditions, such as pressure or temperature changes. Extending vertically through the crew quarters to the quick-opening hatch is a 'fireman's' pole for speedy evacuation in an emergency. In normal circumstances the men will use the pole in the weightless environment to move through the centre of the workshop and transfer equipment from the multiple docking adapter to the work section and laboratory.

As many as 50 experiments were envisaged for the first five flights in the Apollo Applications Programme, the majority of which were earmarked for the first orbital workshop. They were grouped as follows:

Scientific experiments
So27 Galactic X-ray mapping
So61 Potato respiration
So65 Multi-band terrain photography

S069 X-ray astronomy
S073 Gegenschein flash zodiacal light

Technological experiments
T003 In-flight nephelometer
T013 Crew vehicle disturbance
T017 Meteoroid impact and erosion
T018 Precision optical tracking
T020 Jet shoes
T021 Meteoroid velocity
T023 Surface-absorbed materials
T025 Coronagraph and contamination measurements
T027 ATM contamination measurements

Department of Defense experiments
D008 Radiation in spacecraft
D017 Carbon dioxide reduction
D019 Suit donning and sleep station evaluation
D020 Alternate restraints evaluation
D021 Expandable airlock technology
D022 Expandable structures

Engineering experiments
M402 Orbital workshop
M415 Thermal control coatings
M423 Hydrostatic gas bearing
M439 Star horizon automatic tracking
M469 ST-124 guidance system removal
M479 Zero gravity flammability
M487 Habitability/crew quarters
M489 Heat exchanger service
M492 Tube-joining assemblies
M493 Electron beam welding
M508 EVA hardware evaluation
M509 Astronaut-manœuvring equipment

Medical experiments
M070 Nutriona and musculo-skeletal function
M071 Mineral balance

M072 Bone densitometry
M073 Bioassay of body fluids
M074 Small mass measurement
M090 Cardiovascular function
M091 LBNP (lower body negative pressure) pre- and post-flight
M092 LBNP (lower body negative pressure) in-flight
M093 Vectorcardiogram
M094 Anti-deconditioning garment
M130 Neurophysiology
M131 Human vestibular function
M150 Behavioural effects
M151 Time and motion study
M170 Pulmonary function and energy metabolism
M171 Metabolic activity
M172 Body mass measurement

An important aspect of the Apollo Applications Programme is the opportunity it gives for astronomer-astronauts to work alongside telescopes and other astronomical instruments in space. Although important work has been accomplished with unmanned spacecraft, such as the Orbiting Astronomical Observatory (OAO), the opportunities now opening up through manned observatories should bring large advances in our understanding of the Universe.

Astronomers have long desired a stable platform in space from which to observe the heavens free from atmospheric interference and absorption. From a space observatory it is possible to observe a wide spectral band of visible and invisible energy, whereas, previous to orbital astronomy, especially in the 3,000 and 800 Å regime, the atmosphere limited precise study of many objects, not least the great clouds of interstellar matter in the Milky Way.

The Apollo Telescope Mount (ATM) was the first instrument designed for operation by American astronomer-astronauts in the space environment. The five experiments in the first ATM were chosen to obtain measurements of the Sun in the extreme ultraviolet and X-ray portions of the electromagnetic spectrum, which cannot penetrate the Earth's atmosphere, and obtain pictures of the Sun's corona in the white light portion of the spectrum. Later manned observatories will make detailed observations of the stars and other celestial objects across the broad range of the spectrum.

The manned ATM offers opportunities for observation not available with unmanned spacecraft. For example, the astronomer-astronaut can use his own judgement to select objects of scientific interest and point the telescopes accordingly. He can control all ATM operations including the acquisition of data and retrieval of films; and he can also make adjustments and repairs. The various operations can, of course, be supplemented by radio contact with astronomers on the ground who can redirect the observing programme according to ground data or verbal descriptions from orbit. Had all this to be done purely by automatic means, the space observatory would be exceedingly complex and the smallest fault could wreck the entire project.

The Apollo Telescope Mount was designed as part of a cluster of spacecraft to orbit as a unit. It includes the orbital workshop and a manned Apollo command and service module (CSM). The various components are delivered into orbit some 300 miles (481 km.) above the Earth by Saturn 1B space rockets launched from Kennedy Space Center.

First, the unmanned S-IVB workshop is manœuvred into the desired position ready to receive, a few days later, a manned Apollo spacecraft which will rendezvous and dock with it. Its three-man crew must then make the workshop habitable for a stay of 28 days (page 28). After the first crew has returned to Earth, the orbiting workshop is revisited by another three-man crew who conduct medical or other experiments in the workshop for up to 56 days.

Astronomy experiments were planned to begin with the fourth and fifth flights when first a manned Apollo command and service module (CSM) is sent into a preliminary orbit to rendezvous and dock with an ATM. After they are joined, the ATM cabin is manned and the combined vehicles rendezvous with the workshop in its 300-mile (483 km.) orbit.

The arrivals reactivate the workshop and prepare it for its new astronomy role. With the ATM attached at one of the docking points (page 28) the cluster will be inertially stabilized by the control system of the ATM to maintain the axis of the telescope along the Sun line. There are two main control loops. One utilizes a coarse Sun sensor and is stabilized by three large control moment gyroscopes providing basic cluster orientation and stability. The other loop is a fine-pointing system driving the experiment package. Use is made of a very precise Sun sensor to accurately point the instrumentation at specific targets on the Sun as selected by the crew. The vernier control system also serves to counteract disturbances due to crew motions and stabilize the vehicle within $\pm$ 2·5 sec. of arc. Planning for the first ATM observations allowed for a stay of eight weeks in orbit.

Experiments for the first ATM were co-ordinated by the Marshall Space Flight Center at Huntsville, Alabama. They were designed to provide high spatial and spectral resolution in the ultraviolet, X-ray, white light and hydrogen-alpha (6,563 Å) bands of the spectrum. The five principal instruments were: (1 and 2) the High Altitude Observatory white light spectrograph and extreme ultraviolet spectrograph; (3) the Harvard College Observatory ultraviolet scanning spectrometer; (4) a Goddard Space Flight Center X-ray telescope and (5) an American Science and Engineering imaging X-ray spectrographic telescope.

Control of the orbital observatory is performed from the cabin of the ATM which contains appropriate display panels and controls for the pointing system, instrumentation, communications, and power supply. Television allows astronauts to view images of the Sun recorded by the telescopes. Altogether there are six TV cameras in the experiment package and two TV display monitors and associated console controls.

Two of the cameras observe portions of the solar disc through hydrogen-alpha telescopes, using different bandwidths to achieve the necessary discrimination of detail. A third camera observes the whole of the Sun in the extreme ultraviolet. The fourth camera, part of the Naval Research Laboratory experiment B, observes the spectrograph 3×60 arc sec. slit superimposed on the solar disc in white light with a narrow field of view. Camera five is part of the Harvard College Observatory's spectrometer, observing in hydrogen-alpha, in which the spectrometer slit position is superimposed on the solar disc with a narrow field of view. The sixth camera observes the Sun's corona, as seen through the white-light coronagraph occulting optics. Console switches allow the scientist-astronauts to observe the same experiment or two separate experiments at one time.

At any time observations can be matched with information from the ground allowing telescopes to be directed at specific regions of solar activity. When the time comes to change film astronauts will don pressurized suits and go outside through the airlock of the workshop. After retrieval the used film will be stored in the command module of the Apollo spacecraft ready for the return flight.

In developing the Apollo Telescope Mount NASA made use of existing Apollo hardware. The ATM is, in fact, based on the ascent stage of the lunar module (LM) originally designed to lift astronauts from the surface of the Moon. An ingeniously designed telescope rack replaces the descent stage of the original vehicle.

Total weight of the ATM is close to 31,000 lb (14,061 kg.) made up of about 11,000 lb (4,990 kg.) for the 'ascent stage' and nearly 20,000 lb (9,072 kg.) for the rack and its experimental package.

The 'rack' itself is an octagonal truss structure approximately 114 in. (289·6 cm.) deep supporting the ATM experiment package and attaching to the LM ascent stage. In the launch phase aboard the Saturn 1B the rack is fixed to the launch vehicle at the four attachment points originally provided for the lunar module.

At the centre of the rack is a 102 in. (259 cm.) diameter support ring for the gimbal bearings required for fine pointing. The 82 in. (208·3 cm.) diameter cylindrical experiment package is 135 in. (383 cm.) long. The package is divided longitudinally into four equal parts by an interior cruciform structure in which the telescopes are mounted. Circulating in the skin of the cylinder is a liquid coolant maintaining an internal surface temperature of 50° F (10° C) irrespective of whether the observatory is in sunlight or shadow. At the pointing end of the experiment package is a solar shield arranged in such a manner as not to obstruct movement. This protects the rack's electronic components from direct solar heat.

It has also been necessary to mount exhaust deflectors beneath the gas-jet reaction controls of the lunar module to protect the mirrors of the telescopes and other components from contaminants.

The experiment package is attached to the support ring on the

ATM rack by a gimbal device. This allows the cylinder to be moved ± 92° in pitch and yaw and ± 95° in roll and is used for fine pointing. The large control moment gyros, built by the Bendix Corporation, serve as stabilization actuators for the complete workshop cluster. Each ATM embodies three gyros weighing about 400 lb (181·4 kg.) apiece. They have 22 in. (55.9 cm.) wheels revolving at speeds up to 8,000 r.p.m. for pointing and controlling the cluster in pitch, yaw and roll. Fine pointing, as already mentioned, is achieved by a closed loop torque system under the control of a fine Sun sensor package and rate gyros.

Power supply is from a combination of extendable solar cells and rechargeable chemical batteries. The four solar cell arrays have a total area of some 1,200 ft² (111·48 m.²). Electric power generated in the cells by sunlight is fed via a distributor to each of 18 power modules. Each module has its own battery, battery charger, regulator and sensing and control circuitry to achieve the highest possible standards of reliability.

Where will these experiments lead? Numerous discussions with American astronomers led Dr Wernher von Braun to believe that man-monitored observatories offer many advantages over purely automatic ones. Inspection tours of ground-based observatories – most of them built 5 to 40 years ago – had shown 'there was hardly a scientific research programme now underway whose specific objectives were even defined a year ago'. The way most astronomers and astrophysicists go about their business is that they observe something they consider interesting, evaluate their findings, and publish a paper if they run into something they consider of sufficient interest to their colleagues. As these papers may trigger further investigation by a different individual several years after the original publication, von Braun thinks it important to develop permanent facilities in orbit which can accommodate a wide variety of scientific attachments. The basic instrument that was manufactured and lifted into orbit at great cost must be used over and over again for as long as possible; no single research project would possibly justify the cost of the observatory in orbit which obviously would be many times that of Mount Palomar. It will simply not be very attractive to launch a completely pre-programmed unmanned orbital observatory, costing several hundred million dollars or more, into space, use it for six weeks and then abandon it. On the other hand the many different research tasks supported by a manned orbital observatory over a period of years would certainly justify the high cost of establishment. Von Braun envisions such an observatory as consisting of perhaps one or two solar telescopes plus two or three stellar telescopes and radio telescopes. All these units would be clustered around an orbital core where astronomer-astronauts would be housed and facilities provided for study, processing and evaluation of films, and communication with the ground.

> If they are not satisfied with the pictures or spectra they have taken, [he says], they can try again with another setting, another type of film, or another exposure time. After a few weeks or months in their orbital observatory, the astronomers would return to Earth and write their theses. I am led to believe that unless we have such a system, we will not be able to come up with an attractive cost-effective orbital astronomy programme.

CHAPTER THREE

SPACECRAFT AND BOOSTERS

From the first Sputnik to spacecraft for landing men on the Moon, launch systems have depended on rockets whose stages fall to destruction after their work in accelerating the payload is done. If space activity is to be fully exploited in the next decades, the need is urgent to develop new launch techniques which avoid this wasteful procedure.

The biggest and most expensive example of this 'throw-away' philosophy in the United States is the three-stage Saturn 5 developed for the Apollo man-on-the-Moon project. Everything about this huge booster is impressive. Complete with Apollo spacecraft, it stands 364 ft (111 m.) tall, 60 ft (18·3 m.) higher than the Statue of Liberty on its pedestal. Just one vehicle packs enough power to place in Earth orbit all the US manned spacecraft previously launched. It will, in fact, send a payload of 120 tons* into close orbit or 45 tons* to the Moon.

More than 250,000 designers and engineers worked on the various ground test and 15 flight vehicles ordered by NASA, and some 2,000 large and small companies all over the United States supplied parts and services.

An idea of the scale and complexity of Saturn 5 is given on pages 00–00. The (S-IC) first stage, produced by Boeing, is 138 ft (42·1 m.) tall and 33 ft (10·06 m.) diameter. It has a dry weight of 307,000 lb (139,255 kg.) and contains about 4·7 million lb (2,131,920 kg.) of liquid oxygen and kerosene. The five Rocketdyne F-1 engines are mounted in a square pattern with the fifth in the centre. The four exterior engines, mounted on gimbals, can be deflected for thrust vector control. Total lift-off thrust is 7·5 million lb (3,401,900 kg.).

The S-II second stage, produced by North American Aviation, provides 1,000,000 lb (453,590 kg.) of thrust. It is 81 ft (24·7 m.) tall, 33 ft (10·06 m.) in diameter and is powered by five Rocketdyne J-2 engines burning liquid oxygen and liquid hydrogen.

* US short tons.

The S-IVB third stage is produced by McDonnell-Douglas Corporation. It is 58 ft (17·7 m.) tall, 21·8 ft (6·65 m.) in diameter, contains 230,000 lb (104,330 kg.) of liquid oxygen and liquid hydrogen and has a single J-2 engine of 200,000 lb (90,720 kg.) thrust.

Each Saturn 5 costs about $175 million to build and launch plus another $10 million for a cryogenic lunar logistics system. This means that each pound of payload delivered to the Moon works out at around $6,600.

Although some amelioration of this problem may be obtained by designing future launch vehicles on the modular principle, using maximum simplification of basic systems, the ultimate booster must allow for either partial or complete recovery.

The difficulty of recovering conventional ballistic rockets was apparent in studies to see if it was practicable to decelerate and land the S-IC first stage of Saturn 5 in later models. A whole range of possible recovery devices for the 138 ft (42·1 m.) long booster was investigated by the Boeing Company on behalf of NASA's Marshall Space Flight Center. They include a fixed-wing arrangement, parachutes, hydrogen-filled balloons, drag brakes, ballutes (part balloon, part parachute), paragliders, and rotary systems of spinning parachutes. The simplest and lightest method, offering the greatest savings in time and money, was the water impact system using drag brakes and parachutes. Assuming a requirement for 60 launchings over a 10-year period, total savings were estimated to exceed $500 million assuming that each booster could be relaunched at least three times.

Recovery would proceed as follows: after the rocket stage had separated and before aerodynamic forces became effective upon re-entry into the atmosphere, a nose-forward attitude of the S-IC would be maintained by reaction jets. Near the peak of the booster's trajectory drag brakes would lock open at 45°, giving increased drag and improved stability. Further deceleration would result from the booster's blunt nose formed by the end dome of the liquid oxygen tank which would be thermally protected by ablative material. Oxygen tank pressure would be increased for re-entry to improve structural rigidity.

By the time it had descended to 32,000 ft (9,754 m.), the booster would be moving at about the speed of sound. Almost immediately, when speed had dropped to 928 ft/sec. (283 m./sec.), four 6 ft (1·82 m.) diameter pilot parachutes would open followed by four 45 ft (13·7 m.) parachutes at 29,600 ft (9,028 m.). Finally, at a height of 15,000 ft (457·2 m.), four main supporting parachutes, each of 120 ft (36·6 m.) diameter, would blossom out above the booster (page 45).

As the S-IC descended slowly towards the sea, at about 500 ft (152·4 m.), the liquid oxygen tank dome would be explosively separated and vent holes blown in the rear end of the tank so that upon impacting the water at about 100 ft/sec. (30·5 m./sec.) the tank will act as a pneumatic shock-absorber. After landing the booster rotates slowly in the water to assume an engine-down attitude, attaining stable buoyancy, and awaits pick-up by a specially adapted booster recovery vessel.

Sea-water corrosion of vital parts would be countered in different ways. Special epoxy resin paint could be used to protect the booster itself for up to 15 days after landing. Boeing concede that some components such as switches and gauges would need replacement. But, according to the study, most of the electrical and electronic equipment which is adequately sealed could be satisfactorily refurbished by flushing with fresh water and drying with alcohol.

Total weight of the booster recovery system, including four enlarged fins, drag brakes, reaction control unit, and parachutes, would be 48,700 lb (22,090 kg.), which compares with a booster empty weight of about 165 tons.

This, of course, is not the only path to booster recovery, and like so many original concepts in astronautics the idea of the rocket transporter originated in Europe. As long ago as 1933 the late Dr Eugene Sänger sketched a proposal for such a craft in his book, *The Technique of Rocket Flight*, which envisaged flight speeds of 1,600 m.p.h. (2,575 km./hr.) at stratospheric altitudes.

The basic idea of a rocket aircraft capable of extending its range by gliding at high speed in the upper atmosphere was to remain with Sänger for the rest of his life. Before World War II began Sänger was called from Vienna and entrusted with the formation of a Research Institute for the Technique of Rocket

Flight at Trauen, Germany, where his ideas were considerably extended with the aim of producing an 'antipodal rocket bomber' (page 46). The research undertaken at this small establishment, with a team that included mathematician Dr Irene Bredt (later to become Sänger's wife) was remarkable and far ahead of its time. Although terminated in 1942, its general conclusions were to dominate aerospace technology for a generation.

The project began with the construction of laboratories, workshops, a test house, and an office building. The elaborate 10-year experimental programme was aimed at proving the basic technology for a rocket aircraft of revolutionary design. Its wings and fuselage were to be entirely flat on the underside to resist aerodynamic heating as the craft extended its range by gliding at high speed in the upper air.

It was envisaged that a captive booster would launch the rocket aircraft along a monorail track 1·8 miles (2·9 km.) long.* Near the end of the track the booster sled would be braked and ultimately brought to rest while the aircraft took off at about Mach 1·5 velocity, deriving lift from wings and body to climb at an angle of 30°. At an altitude of 5,500 ft (1,676 m.) the craft's own rocket engine would ignite to achieve a ballistic flight path extending 100 miles (161 km.) into space.

Later, when re-entering the Earth's atmosphere, the aircraft would extend its range by the 'skip' technique, following a wave-like trajectory of decreasing amplitude at the fringe of the effective atmosphere. In this way frictional heat was assumed to be re-radiated into space from the aircraft's metal skin.

Sänger appreciated that many fundamental problems would have to be solved before so ambitious a project could be realized, and outlined 10 major areas for detailed investigation: (1) air-loads and the shape of airframes for Mach numbers between 3 and 30; (2) gas flow with simultaneous chemical conversion of the flowing medium; (3) air forces in a large free path of the molecules; (4) fuel research (in particular the burning of light metals, the dispersion and properties of liquid ozone); (5) research on materials (especially those required for liquid-oxygen pumps and high-duty combustion chambers); (6) construction of a high-

* *Astronautics in the Sixties*, by K. W. Gatland, Iliffe Books Ltd, London, 1962.

pressure steam-driven turbo-pump for fuel and oxygen; (7) construction of ignition apparatus for the rocket engine; (8) development of a combustion chamber for extreme gas temperatures at 50 to 100 atmospheres gas pressure, with water-cooled walls and internal steam cooling, thrust 100 tons; (9) development of a supersonic catapult device for long-range rocket aircraft; (10) development of a mathematical theory and calculation of trajectories for long-range rocket aircraft.

Before Sänger's work at Trauen was stopped in 1942, facilities had been created for testing 1-tonne-thrust experimental gas-oil liquid oxygen engines, using continuous water cooling by means of pipes tightly wound around the entire length of the combustion chamber. The combustion pressure was an unprecedented 100 atmospheres.

The effort had progressed sufficiently for work to begin on a full-size thrust chamber of 100 tonnes thrust, and at least a mock-up cooling system was built, consisting as before of tightly coiled tubing. A liquid-oxygen pump intended to supply 4 l./sec. against a pressure of 150 atmospheres was also under development. In support of these experiments the Institute had the largest liquid oxygen tank in Germany with a capacity of 110,250 lb (50,000 kg.).

After World War II ended the advanced ideas of Sänger and his team were fully investigated, not least by Soviet rocket engineers. (See *Astronautics in the Sixties*, by K. W. Gatland, Iliffe Books Ltd, pp. 252-254.) Detailed investigations of launch systems that could be made partly or wholly recoverable occupied the attention of many government agencies and companies. Continuing the line of thinking Sänger had begun in Germany, efforts were made to apply aircraft-type boosters in multi-stage configurations. America's chief advocate of this approach was Dr Walter Dornberger, the former commandant at Peenemünde, who had become a consultant to Bell Aerospace Company in the early post-war years. But the technology – particularly the necessary heat-resistant airframe and wing structures – was not ready to produce the necessary hardware. The payload such vehicles could deliver into orbit would be small in comparison with their launch weight, and for the relatively small number of launchings envisaged it was easier and cheaper to proceed with expendable rockets.

The path to more rational operational space concepts was to prove long and arduous.

The first attempt to build flight hardware for a hypersonic vehicle following principles established by Sänger was made by the Boeing Company of Seattle under contract to the US Air Force. This was the X-20 Dyna-Soar. The name was simply a contraction of the words 'dynamic' and 'soaring', meaning that, in circular motion around the Earth, the vehicle would make use of both centrifugal and aerodynamic lift forces. After an orbital mission, the craft was expected to descend in a protracted glide without 'skipping', with the delta wings and combined aerodynamic and gas-jet controls providing lift and manoeuvrability. Because of the exceptionally high heating rates to be encountered, it was necessary to employ entirely new airframe materials and structural techniques.

After beginning serious study of hypersonic flight problems in 1953, Boeing devoted more than 7,000 hr. of independent research to wind-tunnel testing. Of this nearly 3,000 hr. involved research above Mach 15.

The many diverse shapes studied ranged from low lift-drag ratio capsules recoverable by parachute to variable-geometry vehicles recoverable by wings. One project had 'swing-wings' which gave a swallow-tail appearance at hypersonic speeds but opened out for landing.

However, the shapes that were beginning to interest NASA and the US Air Force were simple wingless shapes having gas-jet controls and the minimum of aerodynamic surfaces. It is only a slight exaggeration, Boeing engineers insisted, that a wooden shoe could be steered through the air merely by banking it. Their studies showed that guidance in the longitudinal and lateral range might be accomplished solely by controlling the bank angle.

Flight control electronics for Dyna-Soar were being provided by Minneapolis-Honeywell. Mostly they were to be based on equipment that had already been developed and tested in other space vehicles. For example, the inertial platform was virtually the same as that used in Centaur, the gyros of which had been in production for some years. Other vital equipment, including a digital coupler and power supply, a guidance-system computer and an automatic flight-control system, were under development.

A major problem had been to devise a control system which was economical in its power demands. The system actually selected made maximum use of aerodynamic controls only when the effectiveness of the aerodynamic surfaces fell below a set value.

The fulcrum of this control system was an automatic gain changer which had an output inversely proportional to the effectiveness of the aerodynamic controls. It operated by phasing in the reaction controls when the output level reached a certain value, and phasing them out when a second predetermined level was reached.

Good 'energy management' is vital to the operation of a manned hypersonic glider, requiring rapid and accurate computation between the amounts of kinetic energy to be dissipated during the drag-braking manoeuvre and the potential energy remaining in the glider for control purposes. These energies must be constantly compared so that the pilot is afforded the very maximum of descent and landing manoeuvrability.

Navigation aids for Dyna-Soar were being developed by General Precision, Inc. Energy management displays resembled small television screens mounted on the instrument panels. Each screen was overlaid with a variety of flight paths giving the pilot a choice of routes to follow. They could be used after an emergency launch abort and during normal re-entry and landing phases.

In this way Dyna-Soar was expected to shorten or lengthen its range by thousands of miles and to manoeuvre thousands of miles to right or left of its flight path to reach base. By combining the high speed and extreme altitude of his spacecraft with the ability to manoeuvre, Boeing claimed the pilot could have the choice of any airfield between Point Barrow, Alaska, and San Diego, California.

It had been proposed to construct the leading edges of Dyna-Soar of ceramic or graphite materials which, in practice, could be allowed to become white-hot. The relatively cooler parts of the structure – only red-hot! – might then be made of one of the high-temperature 'super-alloys' such as coated molybdenum or columbium. A typical structure of this kind made extensive use of corrugated metal to permit the maximum amount of expansion to occur under high-heating. These accordion-type movements were to be supplemented by the use of expansion joints between the skin panels.

Later, it was proposed that vehicles of the Dyna-Soar type might be built with a heavy internal truss framework with pinned connections between joints to permit even expansion. With the highest heating rates experienced at the front of the glider, ceramic zirconium graphite would provide a nose section able to resist temperatures of about 1,909° C (3,470° F), while similar materials and/or refactory metals, such as treated molybdenum and columbium, would be employed for leading-edge sections.

A full-scale Dyna-Soar test-vehicle was being prepared at Boeing's Seattle plant for glide tests from a B-52 bomber near Edwards Air Force Base, California, in 1963–64, but the project was cancelled before this could be completed.

What had finally sealed the fate of Dyna-Soar was not only its growing complexity and cost, but the fact that it was over twice the weight of a ballistic capsule of the same payload capability.

Much research to overcome these problems was subsequently carried out by NASA and the US Air Force with unmanned glide vehicles launched by ballistic rockets.

While model tests helped NASA laboratories evolve new high-temperature structural techniques, experiments in the low-speed handling of lifting-bodies were made with manned vehicles, the NASA/Northrop M2-F2 and HL-10 and the USAF/Martin X-24A (formerly SV-5P).

The X-24A designed for flight speeds up to Mach 2 was constructed conventionally of aluminium-alloy. This flat-bottomed vehicle 24·5 ft (7·47 m.) long has the shape of a bulbous wedge, rounded at the top, with vertical fins. Its maximum fuelled weight is about 11,000 lb (4,990 kg.).

Primary propulsion is by a four-chamber Thiokol XLR-11 rocket engine having a maximum thrust of 8,000 lb (3,629 kg.); propellants are ethyl alcohol-water and liquid oxygen. Two Bell LLRV engines of 500 lb (227 kg.) thrust are available for use during the landing approach.

Pressurized at 3·5 p.s.i., the cockpit has an ejection seat, a jettisonable canopy and conventional-type cockpit controls acting on upper and lower flaps (ailerons and elevators) and twin rudders.

Launched from a B-52 at 45,000 ft (13,716 m.) an unpowered flight takes approximately 3·5 min. Use of the rocket engine extends the flight duration to about 15 min. The landing flare manœuvre occurs at an altitude of about 1,000 ft (304·8 m.) and a speed of 200–300 knots (371–556 km./hr.). Landing speed is between 140 and 310 knots (259 and 574 km./hr.).

Hypersonic flight experiments performed with the sub-scale Martin SV-5D Prime lifting-body gave the US Air Force renewed confidence in the 'multipurpose re-usable spacecraft'. Although the first two models had been lost at sea, good telemetry data were obtained showing that they retained structural integrity in stable flight.

The third vehicle launched on 19 April 1967 was successfully air-snatched by a C-130 recovery aircraft and returned for examination. Despite the fact that the 860 lb (390 kg.) vehicle had travelled at near-orbital speed after separating from the Atlas SLV-3 booster, launched from Vandenberg AFB, California, it was remarkably well preserved.

Reporting on the three flight experiments Colonel C. L. Scoville, director of the Air Force Space Systems Division START programme, said they had proved the re-entry of an aerodynamically controlled vehicle; that ablation effects did not materially affect stability and control, and heating predictions were fully verified. There was 'minimal recession' of the silicone ablative coating which covered the entire body except for highly critical areas such as the nosecap and control flaps which were of moulded carbon phenolic material. The aim was to restrict internal temperature during re-entry to 400° F (204° C).

Telemetry black-out due to the plasma sheath that forms around a spacecraft during re-entry was far less severe than expected. Guidance systems were successfully flight-tested, the vehicle being steered out of plane of the normal descent trajectory and returned to course. The ablative flap system performed as predicted and the value of ground-based terminal guidance was fully demonstrated.

After experience had been gained with piloted lifting-bodies at speeds up to Mach 2, the USAF were anticipating full-scale rocket launching of a modified SV-5P from Cape Kennedy. Calculations were based on the ability of a modified Titan 2 boosting the craft eastward around the world and back to the United States to land at Rogers Dry Lake, near Edwards AFB.

In a NASA-funded study Northrop, too, stressed the importance of extending data by launching a small piloted lifting-body on a Titan 2. This, it was suggested, would obtain the last of the fundamental engineering data for the design of operational craft at minimum cost. The proposed vehicle was similar to the M2-F2 concept, but with sufficient heat shielding to utilize the vehicle's aluminium-alloy structure with a minimum of change. The silica-glass wind shield and canopy would be protected by jettison-able heat shields. Pilot control would be obtained by a two-axis side stick controller, a Gemini-type ejection seat would permit escape from a launch pad 'abort', and landing at Rogers Dry Lake would be made on a ski-type undercarriage.

One of several trajectory-control methods proposed by Northrop – known as the Temperature Rate Flight Control System (TRFCS) – would have the pilot guiding his craft to the desired destination by varying the cooling rate according to temperature data received from thermo-couples installed in the heat shield.

First casualty among the low-speed piloted lifting-bodies was the M2-F2 which crash-landed on Rogers Dry Lake in May 1967. In the accident the NASA research pilot, Bruce A. Peterson, sustained severe facial injuries.

The craft, making its sixteenth flight, had been released from beneath the wing of the B-52 parent aircraft at an altitude of about 45,000 ft (13,716 m.). The flight manœuvres were normal until, coming out of a turn, a lateral oscillation (rolling from side to side) developed and quickly increased in amplitude. Peterson regained control within 11 sec., but by then the M2-F2's approach heading was to the left and angled away from the runway markings on the lake bed. It was necessary for the pilot to immediately begin the landing flare without further heading changes. This left him without the runway-type markings normally used for both landing direction and visual height cues, and raised concern of the possibility of collision with a rescue helicopter hovering left of the runway markings. Adding further to Peterson's difficulties was the fact that the violent roll motion had forced the chase plane pilots to veer a safe distance away and placed them out of position to provide the normal altitude callouts via radio to the M2-F2 pilot.

As a result the lifting-body completed its landing flare just as its vertical descent was arrested and before the landing gear was extended. After bouncing, sliding, and rolling over several times, the craft came to rest upside down. Despite the severity of this accident, it was decided to carry out repairs and modifications and return the craft to service as the M2-F3. Fitted with a centre stabilizing fin and a reaction control system, it was regarded particularly as a test-bed for research into problems of lateral stability and control.

Following a series of glide tests beginning in December 1966, the second NASA/Northrop piloted lifting-body, the HL-10, made its first successful flight under power from the B-52 parent on 13 November 1968. Then came flight tests with the USAF's rocket-powered X-24A (page 55).

One of a number of designs for advanced lifting-body space-craft produced for the US Air Force by Lockheed Aircraft appears on page 55. By contouring the fuselage into an aerodynamic form to give control at both high and low speeds, the large fins previously considered necessary on vehicles of this type have been eliminated. Not only is there a simplified structure and weight saving but a smaller surface area is exposed to extreme temperatures encountered during re-entry. Maximum temperature at the nose can be 5,000° F (2,760° C), and approximately half this value on the body.

Rocket-powered for hypersonic flight in atmosphere and space, the craft would have a small turbojet for low-speed manœuvres and landing; the air intake is forward of the vertical fin with the turbojet in line behind it. The rocket engine, mounted directly beneath the turbojet, is flanked by tanks for fluorine/hydrogen propellants. Slotted in beneath the tanks are 'swing-wings' which extend to ensure a slow-speed touch-down on an airstrip.

Complete launch systems were investigated by many US companies. Typical of two-staged winged concepts employing vertical take-off was the Martin Company's Astrorocket (see page 51). The total launch weight was estimated at approximately 2·5 million lb (1·13 m. kg.). Stage separation was planned to occur at about 40 miles (64·4 km.) altitude at a speed of 8,800 ft/sec. (2,682 m./sec.).

The large first stage then would make a glide re-entry back through the atmosphere, and when drag braking had reduced speed below that of sound at 40,000 ft (12,192 m.) turbo-fans would be started up to propel the lightly loaded craft back to base where it would land horizontally. Meanwhile, having cut off propulsion at about 400,000 ft (121,920 m.) the stage coasts to apogee where the engine is restarted for injection into a 300-nautical-mile (555 km.) circular orbit. The concept aimed to allow three men to remain in orbit for two weeks.

Meanwhile, in Europe, interest in recoverable launch systems had been revived in the early 1960s by the Royal Aircraft Establishment, and certain companies represented in the industrial association of Eurospace.

One early RAE study considered a large piloted aircraft powered by a battery of turbo-ramjets which would reach Mach 7 at 20 miles' altitude. This would serve as the launch platform for a small rocket-powered aerospace vehicle capable of increasing speed to Mach 12–14 at 180,000 ft (54,864 m.).

At this stage the vehicle was looked upon as a specialized reconnaissance-bomber with the eventual prospect of adding a second rocket stage to provide full orbital capability. As a bonus of the research and development effort, a variant of the mothercraft might be developed in the post-Concorde era as a hypersonic transport. This line of development was subsequently abandoned.

However, in this period, Britain did much to stimulate interest in hypersonic air-breathing propulsion in studies by the RAE, Farnborough and Bedford, Bristol Siddeley, Hawker Siddeley Aviation, Rolls-Royce, and elsewhere. The work included wind tunnel, shock tube, and combustion research. A formal agreement between Bristol Siddeley and the Marquardt Corporation linked the work with long-standing US research in this field, allowing for an exchange of information. Pure rocket systems also received attention.

Many of the early schemes, both in the United States and Europe, were for 'piggy-back' arrangements in which launching was vertical with the individual stages transforming themselves into gliders at completion of the boost phase.

Junkers Flugzeug und Motorenwerke contrived to develop the Sänger idea of horizontal launch by rocket sled through a scheme for a two-stage winged rocket (pages 48–49) weighing 187 tonnes at take-off. Estimates suggested this combination could place 2·75 tonnes into a circular orbit at 186 miles (300 km.) altitude.

Sänger had worked on steam rockets to achieve maximum economy for the captive booster, but these involved the electrical heating of water. More recently the Italian Societa Trasporti Missilistici, which had developed a novel low-cost chemical heating system for hot-water rockets, indicated a large reduction in launch costs using their patented method.

A variation on this theme, studied by the West Germany concern of Entwicklungsring-Nord (ERNO) in co-operation with Nord Aviation and SNECMA of France, envisaged the take-off from an airfield of a 170 ft (51·8 m.) long air-breathing booster developing 72 tons of thrust and carrying on its underside an 85 ft (25·9 m.) long winged orbital component (page 51). Separating at Mach 7 speed and 21·7 miles (34·9 km.) altitude, the latter would be propelled by six liquid hydrogen/liquid oxygen rocket engines, four developing 35 tons of thrust each and two 0·7 ton, reaching orbit at 186 miles (300 km.).

In Britain the concept of booster reusability had taken a different path in work undertaken by the Preston Division of the British Aircraft Corporation under contract to the Ministry of Aviation (now Ministry of Technology).

After making a full analysis of various projects and the relative costs of getting useful payloads into orbit, the group chose to examine in detail a unique one-and-a-half-stage rocket system based on the lifting-body principle, but using multiples of almost identical units. Called MUSTARD (Multi-Unit Space Transport and Recovery Device) this had two lifting-body boost units which broke away from a core vehicle of similar configuration which itself continued into orbit. All three lox/hydrogen boost components were intended to return to runway landings.

Such closely identical units could be made on the same jigs and of the same basic materials and this would save large sums of money.

With the lifting-body modules stacked vertically in parallel for take-off, all three units would fire together (page 52). As they accelerated the two outer boost units would feed fuel to the engines of the core; or alternatively, after first-stage boost, fuel would be transferred from the two boost units during a coasting period. At 150,000–200,000 ft (45,720–60,960 m.) the boosts would separate (page 53) leaving the core vehicle to perform the orbital mission. This would allow 3 tonnes of useful payload to be placed in Earth orbit at 300 nautical miles (555 km.) via a 100 nautical mile (185 km.) parking orbit. Take-off weight of the three vehicles was estimated at 935,740 lb (424,492 kg.) with a total propellant load of 775,000 lb (341,540 kg.), each boost unit weighing 311,100 lb (141,115 kg.) and the core vehicle 313,515 lb (142,210 kg.).

To assist their return to base the boost units would embody hydrogen-fuelled turbojets enabling them to fly for 300 nautical miles (555 km.) and eventually land on a runway at just over 100 m.p.h. (160·9 km./hr.). The core vehicle, specially designed to resist severe aerodynamic heating during re-entry, would land back at base in the same way.

A number of factors contribute to the economy of the MUSTARD concept. Only one basic aircraft and one basic rocket engine needed to be developed. The vehicles would have low manufactured weight and there would be minimal ground-erection problems. The concept would be capable of gradual development to full velocity in preliminary sub-orbital flight, and the low staging velocity would simplify booster re-entry and fly-back. Training missions would be possible with a single vehicle, and any particular unit would be capable of self-powered flight.

A cost comparison of the MUSTARD concept plotted against all competitive schemes – each vehicle to carry 2·5 US tons of payload into orbit – indicated that over 10 years' development and 10 years' operation, MUSTARD would put 5,000 tons of payload into orbit for a cost of under $4,000 million. This was 20 to 30 times cheaper than the launch costs of Mercury and Gemini spacecraft.

This interesting British concept was to have its parallel in the United States, except that the recoverable portion of the launch vehicle was configured around a system of cheaply produced expendable tanks.

The expendable tank idea applied to ballistic rockets had been studied by the British Interplanetary Society as early as 1949.* In this case the rocket's cylindrical propellant tanks were divided on the centre-line by light diaphragms and separated by detonating a series of explosive bolts. Thus, the tanks were ejected sideways as the rocket proceeded into space. Simple drop-tank arrangements were also investigated.

The development of thin-gauge pressure-stabilized tanks in the Atlas ICBM – a technique also investigated by the BIS† – put the expendable tank idea into suspension until it was revived in America in the late 1960s.

Coincidentally, the NASA studies were first made public in August 1968 in a lecture presented to the British Interplanetary Society in London by Dr George E. Mueller, NASA's Associate Administrator for Manned Space Flight.

Dr Mueller began by pointing out that using conventional ballistic rockets, the resupply cost for a single three-man orbital laboratory for a year equalled the original cost of the laboratory. The coming era of space stations had led NASA carefully to evaluate resupply systems that would be more economical in routine operation.

Many practical outlets for space stations were already on the horizon. They included survey of the Earth's natural resources, the maintenance of complex equipment in Earth orbit for scientific and commercial purposes, such as astronomical telescopes and broadcasting satellites, spacecraft refuelling, and unique oppotunities for research in the weightless environment – even the

* See 'Initial Objectives in Astronautics', by K. W. Gatland, A. E. Dixon and A. M. Kunesch, *Journal of the British Interplanetary Society*, July 1950, pp. 155–178.
† See 'Minimum Satellite Vehicles', by K. W. Gatland, A. M. Kunesch and A. E. Dixon, *Journal of the British Interplanetary Society*, November 1951, pp. 287–294.

manufacture of certain specialized products in space (page 219).

If these activities were to be fully exploited, Dr Mueller said, not tons but thousands of tons of material eventually would be required to be shuttled in and out of orbit.

Therefore, the first requirement for an efficient Earth-to-orbit transportation system must be an economical space transporter that could be re-used many times with the minimum of maintenance and repair. Ideally, the vehicle should have the operational flexibility of conventional air transports.

A promising design for the 'space shuttle' – extrapolated by NASA from a number of proposals including Lockheed's 'Starclipper' concept – takes the form of an outside lifting-body with drop tanks. This one-and-a-half-stage vehicle would lift-off vertically from a simplified launch pad and return to a horizontal landing on a runway. The large-capacity expendable tanks are wrapped round the vehicle core in a 'V' formation (page 56) forming the nose and sides of the vehicle in the lift-off configuration.

The craft would take off from a small pad at an airbase which, ideally, would be located on the coast. Servicing operations would be more routine than for ballistic rockets. For example, the space shuttle would have all the instrumentation necessary for on-board checkout (page 57) following the practice in large intercontinental jet aircraft. Fault detection in various systems would be automatic. Cryogenic tank trucks, containing liquid oxygen and liquid hydrogen, would refuel the craft on the pad.

Protecting the vehicle from the rigours of re-entry heating is a key problem, but techniques have advanced considerably since the expanding-type metal structures proposed for Dyna-Soar.

Development of a new heat shield was mandatory for manœuvrable lifting-body vehicles. Such craft, flying through the atmosphere after re-entry from orbital altitude, undergo a much longer heating period over their entire surfaces than spacecraft making purely ballistic re-entries. The heat shields of Mercury, Gemini, and Apollo were designed to dissipate far higher heat loads but under much shorter ballistic re-entry conditions. In contrast, the SV-5D re-entry vehicle, after separating from the booster at about 100 miles (160·9 km.) altitude, assumed a re-entry trajectory for recovery some 5,000 miles (8,047 km.) down-range in the South Pacific. It was subjected to re-entry temperatures of between 3,000 and 4,000° F (1,635 and 2,190° C).

Heat-shield protection for the SV-5D was the outcome of seven years of research by the Martin Company in association with NASA's Langley Research Center. It resulted in a new honeycomb design utilizing a flexible ablative material which overcame the unfavourable weight and brittleness of metal or ceramic heat shields.

The honeycomb structure could be bent in multiple directions, a marked improvement over earlier designs which did not permit such flexibility. In practice it could be shaped into panels to fit contours of the spacecraft and bonded to the craft's substructure. The honeycomb, a glass phenolic, gives strength to an elastomeric silicone filler – a rubbery or cork-like ablative material.

This combination of material forms a heat shield which will maintain its shape and soundness throughout all phases of flight. During re-entry, the elastomeric silicone surface forms a hard char rather than being dissipated as gases or molten bits. When subjected to cold it actually becomes more elastic. Environmental tests at Martin showed the shield surface did not recede under simulated re-entry heating and did not shrink, crack, or otherwise fail under the effects of extreme cold.

Moreover, the new shielding allowed a weight saving of about 30 per cent over earlier shields, an important factor when the entire surface of a re-entry vehicle requires an ablative coating.

The concept of the 'space shuttle' which has emerged from this work is a core vehicle which contains all the functional elements for boost and subsequent re-entry plus drop tanks. The tanks contain most of the propellants required for boost.

Three high-combustion-pressure lox/hydrogen engines, mounted in the back of the core, contribute a total thrust in vacuum of 1,050,000 lb. (476,280 kg.). A two-position nozzle allows the engines to achieve optimum high performance for both sea-level and high-altitude operation.

After a vertical take-off the vehicle takes a programmed path over the ocean, releasing the V-shaped drop tanks as soon as propellants are expended. (The tanks are conceived as regular orthotropic shells, supported in such a manner as to preclude any loading but internal pressure.) Separation is accomplished by releasing forward attachments and firing upward-pointing thrusters. Rocket engines, thrusting continuously throughout the sequence, accelerate the separation.

Meanwhile, the lifting-body core continues propulsion into orbit. After necessary orbital manœuvres to rendezvous and dock with a space station and transfer its payload, the craft would be de-orbited by rocket braking to make a semi-ballistic re-entry into the Earth's atmosphere, terminating in a protracted hypersonic glide. The design is similar to the Northrop HL-10 in that flared fins provide directional stability with elevons contributing control in pitch and roll and rudders control in yaw. However, the undersurface of this lifting-body concept is entirely flat.

Severe frictional heating is countered by a special structure combining a rigidized heat shield with lightweight passively cooled insulation (page 57). Dr Mueller emphasizes that this fabrication technique 'paves the way to a spacecraft structural arrangement similar to that of aircraft'. In addition to conventional functions, the basic structure provides backup support for the integrated but refurbishable re-entry heat shield, and attachment and carry-through structure for the drop tanks. The inner skin performs the double purpose of carrying shear loads and acting as a thermodynamic heat sink for the heat shield.

After gliding at high speed in the upper atmosphere the craft will compute its optimum landing path for recovery at the launch site or a major air base. There is the possibility of employing variable-geometry in the form of a subsonically deployed wing as in the lifting-body concept studied by Lockheed (page 55). The landing gear is a conventional tricycle arrangement.

In view of the rigorous conditions which must be endured during re-entry, turn-around time will depend heavily on standardized procedures for repair and replacement of parts and/or equipment. Easy access to replaceable components would be inherent to the design, and checkout of engines and airframe would be accomplished by computerized systems analyses.

Considerable attention has been paid by the Langley Research Center and the Martin Company to the possibilities of replaceable heat-shield panels for refurbishing or renewing spacecraft following orbital flight. Such pre-fitted panels could be easily removed and replaced to permit re-use of the basic space vehicle. The Martin elastomeric silicone ablative material had previously been used by NASA to provide thermal protection for the up-rated X-15 rocket research aircraft which reached speeds of some 5,000 m.p.h. (8,047 km./hr.). A spray-on technique was used to apply the elastomer to the entire surface of the X-15 where temperatures ranged from about 1,300 to 2,600° F (690 to 1,412° C).

According to NASA studies, the space shuttle could carry more than 25,000 lb of payload stored in cargo compartments within the core as well as in external pods. Some typical arrangements are shown on page 58. The assumed vehicle has a lift-off weight of 719,400 lb (326,320 kg.); propellants contribute 589,800 lb (266,933 kg.) and the drop tanks 28,600 lb (12,973 kg.). The lifting-body core has an inert weight of 40,000–44,000 lb (18,144–19,958 kg.) and 50,000 lb (22,680 kg.) of propellants. Overall length is 82 ft (25 m.), overall height including tip stabilizers and extended undercarriage, 24 ft (7·3 m.) and span, over tip stabilizers, 52 ft (15·8 m.). Payload modules slot into a standard compartment between the crew cabin and the propulsion bay in the back of the vehicle.

Propulsion for the Mueller 'space shuttle' would depend on high-combustion-pressure, hydrogen-fuelled rocket engines. Pratt and Whitney, a division of United Aircraft Corporation, have been working for some time on engines of this type under sponsorship from both the US Air Force and NASA. The most advanced work under Air Force contract concerns a high-pressure hydrogen-fuelled engine of 250,000 lb (113,400 kg.) thrust which has a two-position nozzle allowing a single engine to obtain high performance for both sea-level and outer-space operation. Thrust is variable over a wide range.

Another advanced engine concept suitable for recoverable boosters, particularly the semi-ballistic type to be discussed later, is the 'aerospike' or plug nozzle. This type, which has advantages in weight and size, has been under development by the Rocketdyne Division of North American Aviation, Inc. in conjunction with NASA's Office of Advanced Research and Technology and the US Air Force.

In the aerospike engine (page 69), a doughnut-shaped combustion chamber discharges engine gases against the surface of a short centre cone (plug nozzle). This contrasts with the more conventional type of rocket engine in which gases are expanded inside long, bell-shaped nozzles.

The primary flow of exhaust gas is controlled at the outer wall by atmospheric pressure, and acts on the inner wall of the plug nozzle to produce reactive thrust. Secondary flow is introduced through the centre of the annulus of the aerodynamic nozzle, increasing the base pressure and adding to the nozzle efficiency. The result is a short nozzle of exceptionally high performance.

The compact engine unit employs gases tapped from the toroidal combustion chamber to drive the propellant turbo-pumps and uses the turbine discharge for the secondary nozzle flow.

The concept of the aerospike engine emerged from studies of unconventional engines undertaken by NASA's Marshall Space Flight Center. As early as 1966 Rocketdyne displayed a full-scale engineering model of a 250,000 to 400,000 lb (113,400 to 181,440 kg.) thrust aerospike unit of about 8 ft (2·43 m.) diameter and 4·5 ft (1·37 m.) depth. The actual thrust range of the motor could be fixed in development according to the size of throat gap of the ring of tiny chambers along its circumference.

The company found that by combining the advanced nozzle and toroidal combustion chamber, an engine could be made 50 to 75 per cent shorter than the equivalent bell-nozzle engine. It was also possible to employ shorter, lighter interstage structure, allowing the use of larger capacity propellant tanks. And by locating the gimbal point in the plane of maximum diameter, the aerospike could be gimballed within its static diameter to achieve thrust-vector control. Another big advantage was the engine's automatic adjustment to atmospheric pressure providing high performance at sea level or high altitude. This meant the same aerospike engine could be used unchanged as a high-performance booster or upper-stage engine.

This type of engine is the basis of a number of schemes for re-usable launch systems studied by the McDonnell-Douglas Corporation in which the unique plug-nozzle configuration is made to serve both as a propulsion unit and subsequently as a heatshield for booster re-entry and recovery.

Since the plug-nozzle engine is so ideally suited for single-stage orbital vehicles, as well as for ballistic recovery, let us afford it some further attention. The function of a conventional bell nozzle is to convert the heat and pressure energy from the combustion chamber to velocity energy of the exhaust gases. The exhaust flow is constrained by the inside wall of the bell nozzle during expulsion. The larger the (expansion) ratio of exit-area to throat-area, the better is the nozzle capability to produce high-velocity thrust; hence, higher specific impulses and better performance will result. Large expansion-ratio bell nozzles will 'flow full' without being over-expanded during the vacuum conditions encountered at high altitudes. However, the exhaust flow will separate from the internal wall of this type nozzle when operating under the higher (sea-level) atmospheric pressures encountered at lift-off. Accordingly, large expansion-ratio bell nozzles – due to turbulence created in the exhaust stream by flow separation – are very inefficient under launch conditions.

The ideal solution to this problem would be to turn the nozzle inside-out, and allow the exhaust gases to flow along the exterior of an isentropic-expansion 'spike'. The spike surface itself forms one boundary for the expanding flow, and the atmosphere forms the other. The exit diameter (and area) for this type of nozzle, will then be governed by ambient pressure: i.e. high atmospheric pressure at take-off will result in a small-diameter gas stream, and the low atmospheric pressure at elevated altitudes will produce a large-diameter exhaust plume. Accordingly, an automatically adjusting expansion-ratio is acquired, which matches the varying ambient conditions during the entire ascent phase. This device is referred to as an 'altitude-compensating nozzle', because it produces the required small expansion-ratio at sea level, and the desirable large expansion-ratio at high altitudes; maximum performance and engine efficiency is achieved, since it adjusts itself for optimum results at any altitude.

Now let us consider re-entry in a nozzle-down attitude by a revolutionary new type of recoverable launch vehicle to be discussed in detail later in this book. The sharp point of an 'elongated' spike would not survive the brunt of aerodynamic heating any more effectively than would the edge of a conventional bell nozzle. Instead, if the 'spike' is designed as a truncated 'plug', it can then present a more durable 'blunted-nose' configuration to air friction and heat during entry. The truncated plug is now perhaps 20 per cent of its original length; that which was necessary for optimized ascent performance. The removed 80 per cent of the hardware contour can be replaced by using the turbine discharge gases to form the nozzle extension, during powered flight; hence, the nomenclature 'aerodynamic spike', or more briefly – 'aerospike' terminology is used. This configuration of plug nozzle now best satisfies all conditions for powered ascent, as well as for ballistic recovery.

After retro out of orbit, when the vehicle has descended to 400,000 ft (121,920 m.) altitude 11 min. before touch-down, the thermal protection system is activated in a low-flow mode. This system will later cool the base of the vehicle and the external portions of the combustion chamber during the aerodynamic heating phase of re-entry.

Liquid hydrogen is circulated by the turbopump through the tubular wall sections of the plug nozzle. The system operates for approximately 7 min., and during the high-heat phase, which occurs during the final 4 min. of pump operation, a high flow rate of liquid hydrogen will cool the nozzle exterior. After passing through the combustion chamber, the hydrogen is dumped overboard.

In this manner, the lip of the annular combustor is also cooled by the still-cold gaseous hydrogen. This discharged gas (plus the bow shock wave propagated from the blunt nose), will protect those portions of the engine which are exposed to high thermal flux from aerodynamic heating. Since the engines are inoperative during the maximum heating regime of re-entry (they are ignited for terminal velocity cancellation towards the end of the 4-min. period), the hydrogen turbopump will be driven by two solid propellant charges. Thus, sufficient flow will cool the nozzle (and engine) during re-entry, using the same technique which cools conventional bell-nozzle combustion chambers during ascent operation.

But there are additional advantages which the plug nozzle offers over bell nozzles, all of which can be translated into weight savings. As already emphasized, this unorthodox type of engine will be much shorter, more compact, and lighter than a conventional engine producing an equivalent thrust. The direction of the thrust vector from the plug can be controlled, without having to gimbal the entire engine. By increasing the pressure of a segmented combustion chamber on one side of the plug, and decreasing the pressure of one on the other side, the direction of the thrust can be diverted aerodynamically, in an angular direction from the axial centreline of the vehicle. This technique would eliminate the need to use a heavy and complex hydraulic system for actuation-gimballing the very large combined mass of a high-thrust engine and nozzle. It also circumvents the requirement for heavy-thrust structures, since a plug nozzle can be connected rigidly to the periphery of the vehicle (page 64).

Many configurations are possible using this technique in which a ballistic rocket might be made to perform manœuvres under re-entry conditions, in some cases matching the capability of a lifting-body but with greatly improved mass-ratio. Moreover, calculation shows that the new-style recoverable booster could deliver a useful payload into orbit without the necessity for staging or the falling away of any major part of the launch vehicle. Improved payload/weight ratios can be achieved by the use of expendable tanks, which themselves can be parachute-recovered, with the launch vehicle given some lifting capability following re-entry by offsetting the centre of mass (as in the case of Gemini and Apollo spacecraft). If greater manœuvrability is required to achieve a landing far from the plane of ballistic re-entry, variable-geometry can be employed to widen the descent corridor.

A novel solution is offered by the combination of two patented space-vehicle concepts. Although wingless the system would have similar control and manœuvrability following atmospheric re-entry as previously envisaged for winged ferry vehicles.

The essence of the system was patented by NASA in January 1967 on behalf of one of the authors. The proposed Pegasus vehicle (see Chapter Six) has a special type of plug-nozzle engine which, on the return to Earth, becomes a heat shield for the single-stage booster and its integrated pressure cabin. The vehicle's centre of gravity is kept as far forward as possible to ensure stable flight conditions, under re-entry, when the vehicle assumes a backward posture. The plug nozzle is regeneratively cooled by liquid hydrogen both during the ascent period of engine operation and when the 'plug' is taking the brunt of frictional heating on the return to Earth.

The second patented idea – by Robert A. Marshall and Lawrence R. Manoni of United Aircraft Corporation – finds application after re-entry. Whereas in Pegasus eight circumferentially mounted hydrogen fuel tanks are used which jettison during the boost phase, Marshall and Manoni proposed a system in which a similar arrangement of tanks would be retained on the vehicle (in their case a re-entry vehicle with a conventional heat shield) hinging outwards after re-entry to provide a means of modifying the descent path like drag brakes and rudders. The tanks hinged at the heat-shield end, opening out radially by means of a mechanical linkage (page 82).

By spreading one or more tanks on one side, the system could be made to act as an aerodynamic surface giving the vehicle considerable latitude in cross-range and down-range manœuvre similar to that of conventional winged craft. This variable-geometry concept, used in conjunction with a Pegasus-type plug nozzle, would give even more control than conventional aerodynamic surfaces as there would be such large permissible variations in frontal area. Indeed, the effect might have so large an influence on the drag coefficient that the point may be reached where recovery parachutes could be dispensed with. By reigniting a few segments of the plug-nozzle rocket engine the lightly loaded vehicle could be made to hover before touching down on landing legs in the manner of the Apollo lunar module.

CHAPTER FOUR

STEPPING-STONES TO
BOOSTER RECOVERY

From the wide variety of alternative configurations discussed in the previous chapter, it is not yet clear which approach offers the best long-range promise. However, if the next generation of launch vehicles develops on evolutionary rather than revolutionary lines today's space hardware will provide the point of departure.

The first step along this evolutionary path would unquestionably be a mission to demonstrate that the upper stage of a launch vehicle can, indeed, be recovered from orbit. Such a stage should be one that employs advanced cryogenic propellants (liquid oxygen/liquid hydrogen), and which has the capability of achieving orbital velocity. Hence, the Saturn S-IVB stage becomes not only the most attractive but perhaps the only candidate to serve as a test-bed for ballistic recovery. This rationale does not suggest that ballistic, rather than lifting-body or winged, recovery is a foregone conclusion, merely that a continuous development thread can be envisioned for this type of re-usable booster. Accordingly, the present chapter is devoted to this relatively straightforward theme.

Recovery of spent stages from orbit would benefit safety as well as economy; space debris could fall from orbit and imperil densely populated areas of Earth. By mid-1969, more than 3,500 man-made objects had been placed in Earth orbit, nearly half of which remained. Of this number, only about 25 per cent were actual payloads.

This suggests that the orbits of hundreds of spent rocket stages and other space debris will eventually decay to the point where they will present a hazard to populated areas. There appears to be no assurance that entire boosters, including engines, would be incinerated during re-entry. How long will it take for our spaceways to become littered with spent booster cases, if no effort is made to recover them? Some time ago, after the launching of a Gemini spacecraft, a 24 ft (7·3 m.) section of the Titan II rocket, weighing 1,500 lb (680 kg.), was discovered floating in the Atlantic. It was the first major section of a space booster to be inadvertently recovered in reasonably good condition. Two months later, an insulation panel from an Atlas-Centaur rocket also was retrieved from the ocean. Clearly, if portions of a space vehicle can accidentally survive re-entry, without previous protective provisions, minor modifications prior to launch could lead to total stage recovery, including engines. The use of completely recoverable vehicles would increase eventual reliability. Today's commercial aircraft would be less reliable if they had been designed originally as expendable machines.

The development programme leading to an operational recoverable and re-usable booster would probably be implemented in three distinct phases: ocean-recovery of an orbital stage; land recovery of existing hardware; and, finally, redesign of a small cryogenic upper stage to serve as a demonstration test-bed for single-stage operations, as well as semi-ballistic recovery on dry land. During the first phase of the flight-test programme, a minimum-weight ocean-recovery system for the S-IVB would incorporate a modification kit weighing 6,500 lb (2,960 kg.). The scheme is illustrated on pages 60–61. Included in this kit would be propulsion for stabilizing the stage in orbit, retro-rockets for the de-orbit manœuvre, a heat shield for protection during re-entry, and three 80 ft (24·4 m.) parachutes to ease the 58 ft (17·7 m.), 15-ton (13,600 kg.) stage into the sea. Although ocean recovery is easier (since there is three times as much water on the Earth's surface as land), salt-water contamination of the recovered stage will certainly increase the cost of reconditioning this hardware prior to re-use.

The objective of bringing an expended space vehicle back to Earth would be primarily to discover how well it has survived the rigours of launch, re-entry into the atmosphere, and recovery. The data obtained in this manner would be invaluable in assessing refurbishment costs, the major factor which will determine the feasibility of future re-usable rockets. Present cost estimates to recondition a launch vehicle for a second use range from 1 per cent of the original vehicle cost to 65 per cent.

From sea recovery, the test programme would progress to the

second phase – land recovery – developing more sophisticated recovery techniques by further modifications to existing hardware. Land recovery (pages 62–64) would eliminate the complications of ocean-retrieval and salt-water contamination. After a day in orbit, the re-entry corridor would terminate in a prepared landing area staked out near the Atlantic coast of Florida, and some 35 miles (56 km.) north-west of its original launch pad at Cape Kennedy.

The stage would be retrieved from a 150-mile (240 km.) circular orbit, following re-entry initiation by four 6,500 lb (2,950 kg.) thrust retro-rockets. Just before the stage started to re-enter the atmosphere, three 'ballutes' of 28 ft (8·5 m.) diameter would deploy behind the stage for drag braking and stability. Woven from steel-mesh these decelerators would withstand re-entry heating of 2,000° F (1,100° C) for up to 2 mins. The vehicle itself is protected by an ablative heat shield similar to those fitted to contemporary manned spacecraft. Finally, at a height of 30,000 ft (9·140 m.), three 124 ft (37·8 m.) diameter ring-sail parachutes would deploy to lower the S-IVB to the ground. Landing impact and a damaging rebound is prevented by a crushable aluminium honeycomb 'bumper' fitted behind the heat shield.

Four extensible stabilization legs, mounted on the sides of the rocket and extended before landing, would keep the vehicle from tipping over. They would not have to absorb any of the landing shock.

The total weight of the recovered S-IVB would be about 33,400 lb (7,360 kg.). This would include the stage itself, the Saturn instrument unit, and elements of the 7,900 lb (3,580 kg.) recovery kit.

The third and final development phase of the S-IVB-size re-usable booster would necessitate a major redesign to the parent stage, to take advantage of those structural and propulsion advances which have been made during the many years since the initial design of Saturn (see page 64). This vertical-take-off, vertical-landing (VTOVL) device has been named SASSTO, an acronym for Saturn Application Single-Stage-To-Orbit. As the 'vertical-landing' designation implies, this vehicle would be semi-ballistically recovered, on dry land. Such a 'flying machine' would appear unorthodox, since our background experience with aircraft has created a mental image of a recoverable space-launcher similar in appearance to the aeroplane. However, the weight penalty that must be paid for wings during the ascent from Earth seriously reduces the payload that can be delivered into orbit. Yet innumerable USA studies, to say nothing of those produced in Europe, conclude that two winged stages and often three, sometimes with the addition of a rocket-sled launcher, are required to deliver passengers and cargo into orbit.

Ironically, although the concept of a two-stage winged re-usable booster resembles today's aircraft far more than its ballistic counterpart, because its safety depends on the successful falling away of the major portion of the space vehicle, it least duplicates the aircraft's operational characteristics. Moreover, separation of the mated wing surfaces of the two-stage 'piggy-back' arrangement under the high aerodynamic pressures encountered during an emergency 'abort' presents a formidable safety problem.

Only when the winged vehicle can acquire orbital velocity without depending on altitude-start of engines, and without the physical separation of a stage (containing the passenger compartment) during flight, will the attractive operational features of the conventional aircraft have been duplicated in terms of orbital transportation.

Perhaps the principal distinction between the conventional horizontal lander and the vertically recovered booster is related to their operational mode during an aborted flight. In the event of an emergency after lift-off, the VTOHL lifting-body or winged device must reorient itself from the vertical (take-off) attitude into position for a horizontal glide. Moreover, the horizontal lander is unalterably committed to a suitably long runway, which may not be located within range of its glide radius. By comparison, the vertical-lander is not required to reorient itself from the vertical take-off inclination, although they would both require excess propellants to be quickly dumped prior to touch-down. However, the VTOVL device could land in any convenient 'cowpasture'. Further, a SASSTO type of rocket could incorporate, under its footpads, four expendable spherical 'floats' constructed of heat-resistant material. In an emergency, these spherical pontoons would be automatically inflated prior to a retro-supported settling on the ocean. This type of device could, therefore, return to a soft touch-down on land or sea, in the event of an aborted flight. Hence, the VTOVL rocket may, in due course, develop into a commercial transport system with even more inherent passenger safety than today's airliner. This emergency ocean-landing and retrieval technique will be further discussed in Chapter Six.

The SASSTO vehicle would draw upon the latest techniques of rocket construction and propulsion. An exhaustive technical study has shown that extremely lightweight structures can be acquired with liquid oxygen/liquid hydrogen propellants. Hence, it is already possible to produce a vehicle capable of lifting two men into orbit within a standard Gemini spacecraft, while allowing for total recovery of rocket and spacecraft as a unit.

The 62 ft (18·9 m.) long combination-craft would be de-orbited by rocket braking and steered back to Earth over a semi-ballistic trajectory, finally coming down at the pre-selected landing site 'on the hover' like a VTOVL aircraft. Part of the secret of SASSTO's performance lies in the unique combination of a plug-nozzle rocket engine and re-entry heat shield. Use is made of a toroidal nozzle which exhausts at the periphery of a truncated 'plug', cooled by hydrogen circulation. On the return from orbit this 'plug' becomes the vehicle's heat shield. The body configuration allows ample volume for propellants, and the four landing legs are housed in simple fairings along the sides of the vehicle. In the extreme nose might be the Gemini spacecraft or, alternatively, a cargo pod (page 66).

Lift-off thrust of SASSTO would be about 270,000 lb (123,000 kg.); launch weight 216,000 lb (98,000 kg.) and payload delivered into orbit 8,100 lb (3,670 kg.).

Apart from using the vehicle for single-stage orbital operations, it could also be applied as an up-rated replacement for the S-IVB stage. Estimates suggest that a re-usable SASSTO as the second stage of the up-rated Saturn 1 could have increased the payload by as much as 17,500 lb (7,940 kg.). Principally, this results from SASSTO's lower structural weight, the higher propulsion efficiency due to the plug nozzle, and the higher thrust-weight ratio of the engine.

In the final analysis, the issue of winged versus ballistic recovery boils down to one fundamental question: 'How much manœuvrability is required?' By designing SASSTO with an offset centre of gravity and employing roll control during re-entry, a lift/drag ratio (L/D) of 0·5 can be attained. This would allow some 138 miles (222 km.) of cross-range manœuvre and 920 miles (1,480 km.) downrange control, sufficient for most ordinary purposes. The main propulsion unit, now acting in reverse, will provide terminal thrust to cancel the vertical velocity component prior to touch-down on to any level area of ground, eliminating the need for expensive runways.

A combined spacecraft and launcher that can be de-orbited as a unit might find a ready application in satellite repair and logistic missions, delivering consumable items to space stations and transferring crew members between Earth and orbit. A rigorous technical study of such a device, which can satisfy both US and European requirements, would constitute an ideal candidate for a co-operative effort in space between nations.

As mentioned earlier in this chapter, there currently exist about 1,800 objects in earth orbit – approximately 1,350 are space 'trash', and some 450 are US and Soviet satellites. By 1980, it has been estimated that these quantities may increase to almost 5,000 defunct units of orbital 'garbage' and perhaps 1,000 operational payloads. Today, both the useless and the operational orbiting hardware, are beginning to worry the space planners.

Let us first consider the implications of the space debris. Subsonic commercial airliners cruise at an altitude of about 30,000 ft (9·2 km.), where an appreciable portion of Earth's protective atmosphere still exists above them. However, the Anglo-French, Soviet, and American supersonic transports (SST) cruise at twice that altitude. By 1980, spacecraft debris may be falling from orbit toward Earth at the rate of 10 objects per day. When this debris descends to 60,000 ft (18·3 km.), its kinetic energy has not yet been dissipated in the atmosphere. Accordingly, the danger exists for even small particles of orbital scrap penetrating the pressurized cabin of an SST, with disastrous results.

In December 1967 a warning system was implemented in the United States which would notify airline pilots of anticipated falling debris two months in advance of the expected hazard. Commercial flights can now be rerouted during the 20 or 30 min. of danger to the airliner and passengers. Sightings of satellite re-entries are fed into the tracking system by flight crews of 117 different airlines. The Soviet airline Aeroflot is being persuaded to participate in this global warning network.

The United Nations has already ruled that the nation which launches any such orbital debris shall bear the financial responsibility for all damages resulting from destructive impact. Indeed, this astute international body may within the next decade legislate that all launching nations must remove their own depleted upper stages from orbital altitudes where manned space stations will be operating. In addition, all launching nations may be required to provide assurance that their sub-orbital booster stages will fall harmlessly into the ocean. Moreover, it may not be too far-fetched to speculate that a world-wide consortium of commercial airlines would pay a premium for removal from orbit, of such a definitive hazard to human lives and their multi-million-dollar equipment. This could result in one more commercial application for the re-usable booster.

With some major modifications to the payload compartment, the SASSTO vehicle could be converted to a versatile rocket called SARRA, an acronym for Saturn Application Retrieval and Rescue Apparatus. The most important utility for SARRA might not be commercial at all, but rather for a humane purpose; i.e. space rescue of incapacitated astronauts or cosmonauts. Nevertheless, let us examine the projected value for the second type of orbiting hardware – the useful variety. Previously, much discussion has been devoted to delivery of payloads *to* orbit. Let us now consider the postulated traffic returning *from* orbit.

Historically, the most revolutionary devices conceived by man have been developed for – what later proved to be – precisely the *wrong* reasons. Similar artificial stimuli may one day lead to the evolution of an operational space rescue system. Indeed, the cumulative value of defunct unmanned satellites may prove to be the truly compelling incentive for development of a commercial transportation system, one with the capability of returning in-operative orbital hardware back to Earth. Such inoperative satellites could later be reconditioned and subsequently relaunched for additional orbital duty. By 1980, it has been estimated that approximately $5,000 million dollars' worth – constituting a virtual 'gold mine in the sky' – of unmanned spacecraft in various degrees of disrepair, will be orbiting our planet. Hence, a real and tangible motivation, rather than the nebulous preparations for a space emergency, may bring about the need for a new-generation booster. Development of an 'orbital scrap-collector' vehicle, which could later be adapted for returning human cargo to Earth, may eventually be justified on a cost-effectiveness basis.

In a gross sense, the size of the SARRA device, like SASSTO, would also be comparable to the Saturn S-IVB stage; that is, it would weigh about 216,000 lb (98,000 kg.) and have a diameter of 260 in. (6·6 m.), using oxygen/hydrogen propellants.

Like SASSTO, SARRA would incorporate an advanced high-performance plug-nozzle engine. By itself, SARRA could operate as a re-usable single-stage-to-orbit vehicle for resupplying space stations in low Earth orbit with 8,100 lb (3,670 kg.) payloads. It could then return to Earth for a dry landing on four extensible legs, employing retro-thrust for vertical velocity cancellation. Indeed, it is principally this re-usable feature of the launch vehicle design which would permit the booster's application to space rescue missions, since man himself has been designed for re-usability, after successfully accomplishing his space mission objectives.

Conceivably, progressively higher-energy missions could be accomplished by (a) launching SARRA on top of the first stage (S-IC) of Saturn 5; (b) launching SARRA by the lower two stages (S-IC plus S-II) of Saturn 5; and (c) launching SARRA by the entire three-stage Saturn 5. In this manner, the rescue device could be provided with progressively larger increments of velocity capability, to acquire a wide spectrum of Earth-orbital inclinations and altitudes, including synchronous equatorial orbits.

A few space emergencies might develop when sufficient time exists to permit the launching of an Earth-based 'space ambulance.' Such eventualities could also be potential SARRA applications. Although, generally speaking, an ailing astronaut would be rescued through extra-vehicular activity (EVA) from his spacecraft, in some cases it may be possible for retrieval and return of the entire disabled capsule, along with the incapacitated astronaut(s). Such hardware-retrieval capability would have many clearly defined commercial implications. Additionally, on a typical extended-duration mission (a three-day lunar round trip) SARRA might be deployed for returning an injured or incapacitated astronaut from the lunar surface.

Any cursory assessment of high-energy rescue missions, when viewed in consonance with other likely space-retrieval requirements, would indicate that a limited number of deep-space emergencies need not be viewed with total despair. A combined booster/spacecraft, designed with suitable mission flexibility and re-use capability, may prove economically feasible for application to a large number of currently planned missions, as well as to many unpredictable emergencies.

Of the 1,000 operational payloads which have been projected for 1980, some 230 might be communications satellites, in various earth-orbital altitudes. The majority of these complex devices can be expected to cost from $20,000 per lb ($44,000 per kg.) to $50,000 per lb ($110,000 per kg.). Such an extravagantly expensive mechanism would be comparable to the now-defunct, $50-million Orbital Astronomical Observatory (OAO 1), launched in 1966. This satellite is still in a perfect 500 nautical miles (930 km.) orbit, with an inoperable power supply. Accordingly, these postulated satellites for communications, observation, scientific, and navigational requirements of the mid-1980s may collectively constitute an 'entrepreneurial' dream. At an average cost of $10 million each, their cumulative potential value would run into millions of dollars. The cruel facts of history appear to confirm that – in a word – *profit* could well provide the true incentive for development of an effective space retrieval system.

The 164 nautical miles (304 km.) orbital altitude is of extreme interest to space planners, since it is the circular orbit altitude at which the Earth Orbital Space Lab (EOSL) will probably operate. The 19,350 nautical miles (36,000 km.) altitude is perhaps even more significant, because it constitutes the Earth-synchronous orbit altitude which will eventually contain the majority of tomorrow's communications satellites. In all cases, SARRA would be provided with at least 2,000 ft/sec. (2,190 km./hr.) velocity capability for in-orbit rendezvous and rescue manœuvres. Additionally, it would have velocity capability for orbital ejection, and for retro-rocket, soft-landing on Earth. In many cases, the SARRA rescue craft would contain reserve propellant to impart the 13,000 ft/sec. (14,200 km./hr.) necessary for rotating its orbital plane through 30° – the inclination angle between a typical 'parking' orbit for US launches from Cape Kennedy, and a representative USSR orbital inclination. Hence, in certain cases of emergency, SARRA might be adaptable to cosmonaut rescue.

Clearly, any launch configuration must be matched in energy content to the basic mission for which it provides back-up rescue capability. Further, the rescue launch vehicle must be maintained in a manned standby mode, checked-out and ready on its launch pad. Propellant tanks must continuously be topped, ready for an immediate dispatch. The vehicle's guidance parameters must be predetermined and set for the general rendezvous destination. It must be recognized, however, that arrival at the disabled craft prior to expiration of survival time certainly cannot be assured for all emergencies. Clearly, available time (and required energy for rescue) will vary due to the fact that the Earth, with the launch site, rotates below the orbital plane which contains the disabled craft. However, these exacting conditions need not preclude a compromise solution to a potential space rescue dilemma.

If the SARRA rescue craft were launched by the entire three-stage Saturn 5, it would then have the capability of rendezvous (within 1·5 days) with a stricken spacecraft in lunar orbit. It could also be capable of soft-landing on the Moon, and returning to Earth with three astronaut passengers, in addition to its two-man crew, within three days. Upon return, the SARRA vehicle would be recovered on Earth by using precisely the same technique (vertical-descent and retro-thrust) as its lunar-landing mode. Therefore, this type of (semi-ballistic) Earth-recoverable booster can readily land on the Moon's surface during a manned rescue (or a cargo delivery and return) mission, a feat which the conventional horizontal-landing winged vehicle would find impossible. (The latter device would require an unavailable lunar-landing runway, and a non-existent lunar atmosphere to provide lift.)

The structure which serves as a nose-fairing during Earth-launch of SARRA would be constructed of four hinged segments. These hinged panels could be opened in orbit, exposing an internal latching device – an automatic clamp universally adjustable to a multitude of spacecraft configurations. After an unmanned communications satellite (or a manned space capsule) has been retrieved, the hinged clamshells would be closed to form the aft portion of the SARRA entry vehicle.

In this manner, the recovered space hardware can be returned to Earth by the rescue craft, and protected from entry heating by the parent launch/re-entry vehicle. It must be emphasized at this point, that this type of operation cannot be duplicated by the relatively small-diameter winged (or lifting-body) category of re-usable spacecraft. Unquestionably, inoperative satellites could be 'serviced' in orbit through extra-vehicular activity (EVA) by astronauts in space suits; but not without great difficulty!

The SASSTO/SARRA type of single-stage-to-orbit vehicle provides the optimum solution to the problem of total recovery of hardware; i.e. no booster stages would be 'dumped' into the ocean after lift-off. However, an alternate method has been investigated, which would also circumvent the extravagance of throw-away space hardware. This technique would make use of a 'captive' lower stage for imparting a sizeable increment of velocity to a spacecraft, without the stage being released from the Earth's surface. This attractive 'captive' booster would be a rocket-sled device called Hyperion. Illustrations on pages 70–71 show the proposed arrangements of sled and space vehicle.

The SASSTO/SARRA orbital rocket, prior to launch, would be supported on the sled in a horizontal position. The Hyperion sled would not be a full 'stage', since it would contain merely propellants; the orbital-rocket motors would provide propulsive thrust. This passenger-carrying rocket could streak across a valley floor and up the side of a mountain to launch itself on a ballistic flight to a destination half-way around the world, or to an Earth-orbiting resort hotel of the future. The 'slingshot' sled device for the single-stage rocket would be supported on an air cushion during take-off while travelling along dual tracks at 680 miles/hr. (1,090 km./hr.). The air cushion reduces sled friction on the track.

Advantages of the sled launch-assist technique would be improved performance of the rocket, and full re-usability of all portions of the entire system. The 8,100 lb (3,670 kg.) orbital payload of the SASSTO/SARRA would increase by 1,600 lb (726 kg.), or 20 per cent, with launch augmentation of 1,000 ft/sec. (1,100 km./hr.) produced by the subsonic sled. Travelling at an average speed of 17,000 miles/hr. (27,400 km./hr.), the sub-orbital rocket could travel from London to New York in only 26 min. Travellers would be subjected to no more than 3 *g*'s during sled-assist take-off up the mountain-side, during powered ascent, or during atmosphere entry and vertical landing. Up to 5 tons (4,540 kg.) of cargo could be hauled in freighter versions of the sled-assisted orbital-global transport.

In a typical launch, the Hyperion re-usable sled which augments boost velocity, could be about 40 ft (12·2 m.) long and 30 ft (9·3 m.) wide. The SASSTO/SARRA engines ignite, driving the sled along the 2 miles (3·22 km.) stretch of level track and up the mountain-side, following the curved track for 1 mile (1·61 km.) before the transport separates from the sled and proceeds vertically on its ballistic trajectory. Free of the rocket, the sled would continue up the track, with retro-rockets, brakes, and gravity combining to stop it.

During the sled's high-speed run, the rocket vehicle would draw its liquid oxygen/liquid hydrogen propellants from tanks on the sled. As the SASSTO/SARRA separated from the Hyperion sled, propellant supply would be transferred to the rocket's internal tanks.

The Hyperion rocket-sled, although offering many impressive advantages, suffers from one major detriment. It would restrict construction of commercial rocket spaceports to only those locations where 1 mile (1·61 km.) high mountains were available. Accordingly, use of rocket sleds would probably be restricted to flight-test programmes only. Such a technique is therefore not envisioned as the optimum operational solution to the commercial passenger rocket: the recommended system, Pegasus, will be discussed in Chapter Six.

In summary, then, what can we conclude regarding the relative merits of semi-ballistic versus lifting-body recovery of boosters?

Primarily that the latter offers greater manœuvrability. But manœuvrability need not be obtained aerodynamically; it can also be acquired propulsively. If, for the sake of illustration, a 900 nautical mile (1,670 km.) cross-range capability were really required, a six-man lifting body spacecraft would weigh 10,600 lb (4,800 kg.) more than an equivalent six-man modified Apollo (ballistic) configuration. When this entire weight differential is converted to propulsive power for manœuvring during atmospheric entry, the ballistic spacecraft would possess 40 per cent more lateral range capability than its lifting-body counterpart. When this comparison is based on equivalent lateral-range-capability, the ballistic vehicle can return a payload from orbit equal to an additional 25 per cent of its empty weight, whereas the lifting-body spacecraft can only be recovered without payload.

As an added consideration, the operational simplicity of the single-stage device would incur a much shorter turnround time than the two-stage vehicle, which necessitates remating of both stages prior to relaunch. This factor of decreased reaction time tends to diminish the number of vehicles (and launch facilities) required in the national inventory. Moreover, with only one stage required to attain orbital velocity, vehicle development costs are reduced, since only a single set of tanks and engines need be developed. Use of only one set of tanks and engines also minimizes the cost of ground-support equipment.

There is also the matter of static stability. An aeroplane is not aerodynamically stable (i.e. it will not glide) unless its centre of gravity (CG) is forward of its centre of pressure (CP). The large concentrated masses of rocket engines, turbo-pumps, etc., are located at the aft end of the lifting-body for propulsion during ascent. This situation consistently places the CG aft of the CP during re-entry; and consequently the vehicle is prone to instability. By comparison, the semi-ballistic vehicle, with its engines and high concentration of mass located forward during re-entry, assures an aerodynamically stable configuration.

With these considerations in mind, let us now examine the prospects for developing realistic systems of rocket transportation.

CHAPTER FIVE

TRENDS IN CARGO TRANSPORTATION

Before anything as revolutionary as the rocket transport can take its place alongside other established systems, it is necessary to demonstrate more than mere technical competence. Alongside obvious advantages in range and speed must be considered manufacturing costs and operating economics. This raises complex questions.

As previously discussed, a step-by-step development programme will undoubtedly be implemented, starting with modified expendable hardware, for demonstrationg technical and economic aspects of booster recovery. But this evolutionary process must be directed toward verifying the eventual characteristics and operational mode of the end-objective configuration. Accordingly, the most attractive type of rocket transport must be identified before the development programme can be initiated: but, what form will it take? Should it be chemically propelled – semi-ballistic, lifting-body, or winged? Or should the development programme perhaps be postponed until nuclear-propelled aircraft technology is firmly in hand? Indeed, this latter candidate could best satisfy the goal of attaining orbital velocity with a single stage. However, the radiation hazards to ground-crew personnel, the severity of atmospheric contamination, and radiation effects on the flight crew, must first be resolved. Before a decision is taken regarding the *type* of rocket transport, the *need* for such a device must be established.

It should be emphasized at the outset that the rocket transport is not proposed as a replacement for aircraft or any of the other contemporary forms of transportation; the rocket-propelled carrier would supplement already existing transport systems. The commercial rocket may not even become a serious competitor to the SST. Many modern transportation devices already exist, side by side, and prosper in a highly competitive market. The most valuable commodity offered by rail over ship, truck over rail, or air over truck, is the progressively decreasing transit time.

Advances in air technology have made us all recipients of the gift of time; space technology will amplify this gift to unexpected dimensions. From one viewpoint, it might be said that the ultimate product of the US-European aerospace industry is time – time gained through more rapid transportation. Accordingly, the passenger rocket could present the priceless gift of one day or more to a high-level executive, each time he had to travel a minimum distance of 8,000 miles (12,900 km.). How much would a day's time be worth to an affluent traveller of the mid-1980s?

We already have the example of the supersonic transport (SST) which offers only one principal advantage over the subsonic commercial jet, namely speed! And yet, billions of dollars have been spent in four countries to satisfy this singular motivation. Clearly, the SST does not provide greater economy, comfort, or safety for the traveller. Accordingly, in our rapidly expanding space age, it appears that the rocket transport, which would further reduce the transit time of air cargo, could find a definite place in the total transportation spectrum for rapid movement of high-priority goods and personnel.

Nor is it suggested that, at its inception, the rocket transport will be used for ranges shorter than transcontinental. Spaceports are not initially envisioned at locations where the distance between each terminal is less than 2,500 miles (4,030 km.). Only after this revolutionary machine had proven itself would a more extensive world-wide network of terminals be established.

As long ago as January 1959, before the United States House of Representatives Select Committee on Astronautics and Space Exploration, James M. Gavin, vice-president of Arthur D. Little, Inc.* declared:

> Mail may someday become almost as swift as the telephone. In the near future [he commented], when guidance devices permit – soft landing, rocket cargo and passenger transport will become feasible. We will probably reach the time when we can consider rocket transport superior over the airplane, for anything over a thousand miles or so – just as we have long since reached a point of recognizing that planes are superior to automobiles for distances over a hundred miles.

*Formerly, Chief of Research and Development, US Army.

In view of General Gavin's prophetic words, let us examine the movement of cargo by conventional means, over a typical trans-continental distance, let us say, from New York to Los Angeles. By surface vessel down the Atlantic coast, through the Panama Canal, and up the Pacific coast, the freight would have to travel some 6,000 miles (9,660 km.); further than from New York to Cairo. By rail or truck the distance between New York and Los Angeles would be about 3,000 miles (4,830 km.), or by air, about 2,500 miles (4,000 km.).

To ship cargo over these distances on ocean-going craft would cost about $30·00 per ton ($0·03 per kg.), requiring some 15 days in transit. By rail, the same distance could be travelled in about 7 days, costing approximately $35·00 per ton ($0·04 per kg.). A truck could haul this cargo in 5 days, for about $90·00 per ton ($0·09 per kg.). By air, the same cargo could be transported in only 5 hr., but the price would increase to $400·00 per ton ($0·44 per kg.), for delicate freight such as electronic equipment. In spite of being the most expensive, air cargo transportation has shown impressive prosperity and growth in recent years. It appears very clear that the public is willing to pay a premium for rapid transit of certain high-priority cargoes.

Estimates suggest that between 1970 and 1980, international air passenger miles will have doubled; and quadrupled by 1985. But air cargo traffic is growing even faster than passenger traffic. By 1980, air cargo revenues may very well surpass passenger revenues, and thereby create an industry many times its present size. In the next decade, air-freight ton-miles could multiply tenfold.

Let us now express the previous costs in terms of transporting a ton-mass over a fixed distance of a mile (or kilometre). To transport agricultural machinery or car parts over the 3,500 miles (5,630 km.) between London and New York, the cost of subsonic air-freight today is equivalent to $0·20 per lb ($0·44 per kg.), or $0·11 per ton-mile. Conceivably, over the next two decades, the rocket freighter could transport high-value goods over such inter-continental distances, at a cost of $0·32 per ton-mile – and in just over 20 min.! Hence, the rocket would cost almost three times more than air cargo, but it would be *15 times faster*. Without doubt, sufficient perishable products exist which will demand these speeds, even at appreciably higher charges.

To underline the promise of future freight rockets, John W. Mahoney, President of Seaboard World Airlines, the fastest growing all-cargo airline in the US, recently startled a New York meeting of the Aviation and Space Writers Association by this visionary forecast: 'I'll predict that rockets – yes, actual rockets – will be used generally for cargo before the SST becomes an airfreighter.' This astounding prognosis was based in part on Mr Mahoney's pessimism regarding the cargo capabilities of the SST. He went on to state: 'I am confident the SST will be of no immediate value in the freight field. The small speed advantage (over the subsonic jet) will be of little economic value, the payload too small, and the fuselage configuration will make it practically useless for volume freight carriage.' Mr Mahoney made it clear that, for the decades ahead, his company requires larger payloads than the 30 tons (27,200 kg.) handled by turboprop transports, and the 40 tons (36,200 kg.) which can be delivered by turbojet aircraft. While the audience of newsmen were recovering from the shock Mr Mahoney went on to tell them, 'you may already know that the US Army has developed an accurate rocket delivery system for supply of front-line troops'.

The conjectural aspects of Mr Mahoney's profound statements essentially comprise the theme of this chapter: is there a cargo or passenger market potential for a rocket vehicle? In a sense, the two are inextricably woven together; i.e. market development depends in large measure on the proper vehicle, and justification for development of the proper vehicle depends in large measure on the market potential. Nevertheless, let us attempt a definitive assessment of where these transportation trends may lead.

In terms of weight and distance, more than two-thirds of the freight transported in the United States and Europe travels overland. Less than one-third is transported over water, and less than one-hundredth by air. If the rocket transport could capture even one-tenth of the total air cargo market, an economic rationale for its development can be justified.

Improvements in transport systems have naturally been paced by the methods of propulsion available at the time. Man first depended on wind power to sail the oceans. After that came steam. The steam-engine allowed him to travel overland by rail rather than by the much slower animal power. The development of the internal combustion engine led to automobiles and early aircraft. Our modern jet-engine provided man with the capability for a quantum jump in speed. Now the rocket engine promises to expand his speed spectrum a hundredfold.

In pre-Sputnik days, before the space age was really born, high-altitude-sounding rockets consumed many hundreds of pounds of propellant for each pound or sub-orbital payload. The four-stage Scout vehicle, which was developed during the late 1950s period of space-age infancy, consumed 255 lb (115 kg.) of solid propellants per lb of payload it boosted into orbit. In the early 1960s, the two-stage Thor-Agena D, which used 'storable' liquid propellants in its second stage, consumed 72 lb (33 kg.) of propellant per lb of orbital payload. In those days, even the most optimistic space engineer would not dare to predict that the three-stage Saturn 5 burning liquid oxygen and kerosene in its booster and lox/hydrogen in upper stages, could reduce this parameter to 22 lb (10 kg.) of propellant per lb of payload. However, the trend had become established. Its direction was clear and indisputable. Engineering progress since 1962, when the Saturn 5 programme was initiated, assures us that the next generation of chemically propelled rockets could reduce this performance index to 14 lb of propellant (or less) per lb of orbital payload. This new breed of re-usable vehicle would burn liquid oxygen and liquid hydrogen. And it could acquire orbital velocity with the improved reliability offered by just *one* stage.

This impressive upward trend in performance can best be explained in terms of advancements in propulsion and light-weight structures technology. For example, the oxygen/alcohol propellants of the V-2 rocket could produce a specific impulse of only 280 sec., at sea level. This means that 1 lb (or 1 kg.) of these liquid propellants generated a thrust of 1 lb (or 1 kg.) for the brief duration of 280 sec. By comparison, 1 lb of liquid oxygen and liquid hydrogen propellants can produce a thrust of 1 lb for 464 sec., under vacuum conditions. This latter specific impulse value can be obtained with higher combustion chamber pressures, increased propellant mixture ratios, and extremely large expansion ratios for engine nozzles. The type of nozzle offering the largest practical expansion ratios is the 'plug' or altitude-compensating nozzle (page 69). Although this type of nozzle can be easily installed on a cylindrical booster, it is difficult to incorporate into a lifting-body configuration.

Moreover, the tanks, pumps, motor, etc. of the V-2 accounted for an inefficient 25 per cent of the total stage weight. Light-weight structures technology has made such enormous strides during the 27 years since the V-2 was first launched, that the combined weight of conventional booster structure and complete rocket engine would constitute merely 7·6 per cent of the stage mass. This phenomenally low figure would include the weight associated with a recovery system. The less efficient type of lifting-body structure, on the other hand, could account for as much as 22·4 per cent of the total stage weight, which explains why the lifting-body is sometimes referred to as the 'flying anvil'.

It has been stated by some of the most erudite observers of our times that speed – perhaps more than any other single index – provides the best measurement for the rate of human progress. In view of the significance of speed throughout the course of mankind's history, this subject warrants significant emphasis. In our present age, applications of advanced technology, initially for military purposes, have increased speeds beyond 1,800 miles/hr. (2,200 km./hr.) which are now commercially available in the supersonic transport (SST), which will cruise at a speed of Mach 2·7, and 60,000 ft (18·3 km.) altitude. It is significant to note that military needs, which do not usually necessitate rigid economic justification, have led to the really impressive advances in aircraft technology. Without doubt, this situation will also prevail with the rocket transport.

The energy required to achieve orbital velocity is grossly comparable to that required for travelling ballistically half-way around the globe (about 12,500 miles (20,000 km.)). Hence, only in recent years, due to major progress in rocket technology and design, has rocket-propelled global transportation begun to appear economically feasible.

By comparison, it is interesting to note that the 334-passenger subsonic DC-10 consumes about 147,000 lb (66,000 kg.) of fuel in carrying 40 tons (36,200 kg.) of payload, or 1·84 lb of kerosene per lb of payload; but that weight figure is applicable to maximum ranges of only 3,200 miles (5,150 km.). Hence, when the range of a typical commercial aircraft is quadrupled to make it comply with non-stop rocket distances – half Earth's circumference – the advanced rocket of tomorrow requiring 14 lb of fuel per lb of payload would appear at least half as cost-effective as today's aircraft, requiring 7 lb of fuel per lb of payload. Therefore, it might be presumed that the operating cost, and cargo or passenger fares, should eventually be twice as high for the rocket than commercial air travel. However, this may not yet be the case. The reason is primarily associated with the more expensive rocket propellants required.

In air transport operations, there traditionally exists a constant ratio (3:1) between total operating cost and fuel cost. Let us assume that some day rockets will be dispatched towards their destinations with as little preparation prior to flight as an aircraft. Accordingly, the rocket will be able to compete with the aircraft only when the fuel costs are approximately equal. But kerosene costs as little as $0·02 per lb ($0·04 per kg.). Liquid oxygen can already be extracted from the atmosphere for $0·02 per lb. But at present large quantities of liquid hydrogen cost $0·25 per lb ($0·55 per kg.). Fortunately, tomorrow's rockets will use a mixture of seven times as much of the cheaper oxygen, than the more expensive hydrogen, resulting in a cost of $0·05 per lb ($0·11 per kg.). Therefore, when hydrogen production cost can be reduced threefold, the commercial rocket should rapidly emerge as a practical reality. It is encouraging to note that an applicable manufacturing process has already been patented. This process would obtain liquid hydrogen from natural gas, rather than extract it from crude oil, as is the current procedure. This new process has the potential of eventually producing liquid hydrogen for as little as $0·09 per lb ($0·20 per kg.). From all indications, then, the commercial rocket transport may be nearer to us in time than was the commercial jet transport just before the Space Age began.

But what will it cost to develop and manufacture this radical vehicle? The answer is very strongly influenced by the size and payload capability. Technical studies have shown that a re-usable vehicle similar to the SASSTO/SARRA as described in Chapter Four, with an orbital payload capability of 4 tons (3,630 kg.), would cost $1,100 million to develop. If 50 were built, each would cost about $16·10 million.

A scaled-up version of Hyperion five times larger than SASSTO/ SARRA might be more suitable for commercial cargo transport. This size vehicle with its 20-ton (18,100 kg.) orbital payload would cost about $1,500 million to develop, and $40 million per copy. As frightening as these costs may appear, they are of the same general magnitude as the SST, and yet cost did not prevent development of this vehicle. For the sake of comparison, all three SST's – the Anglo-French Concorde, the Russian Tupolev Tu-144, and the American 2707-300 – have been assumed comparable in cost and performance; i.e. 260 passengers over a distance of 4,000 miles (6,440) km.).

Since the useful payload of this larger Hyperion rocket can be converted to the equivalent of 110 passengers, it has been estimated that each round-trip ticket to orbit (or ballistic hop half-way around the globe) may eventually cost slightly over $3,000. It should be noted that compared to aircraft, the return trip of a rocket from an orbiting space station constitutes a bonus since fuel costs are non-existent. Indeed, should Earth orbit emerge as a popular tourist destination, such a mission would become the exclusive domain of the rocket; the air-breathing aircraft could not operate above the atmosphere to capture a portion of this commercial market. In that event, we should have no choice, irrespective of economic considerations, than to develop the Inter-Continental Ballistic Transport (ICBT).

Equally as significant as the cost implication is the aspect of unqualified public acceptance of any revolutionary new transport system. The sonic boom problem – the largest single threat to the success of the supersonic transport – constitutes an enormous engineering challenge. 'Boom carpets' 60 to 100 miles (96 to 161 km.) wide may seriously restrict the SST's permissible overland routes. Unless its resulting ground overpressure can be reduced to within acceptable limits of not more than 2·5 lb/ft^2 (12·2 kg./m.^{2}) the SST may eventually be limited to transoceanic flights only, severely compromising the economic payoff. The pressure field, experienced on the ground as a sharp crack or boom, is generated by the shock waves propagated from the SST's nose and tail during horizontal flight. It is this characteristic – the *horizontal* flight of the SST – which is worthy of note. During level flight the damaging and disturbing effect of the boom is felt by population centres along the entire flight path. Mr Bo Lundberg, a Swedish aeronautics expert, has estimated that each SST flight across the United States would lay down a 'boom carpet' assaulting the eardrums of 10 million people, and disturbing millions more. Professor Karl Ruppenthal, director of Stanford University's transportation management programme, recently commented: 'Both the governments of Germany and Switzerland have said already that they will forbid SST flights over their territories, if their populations find them to be annoyances.'

It has been determined from past studies that any horizontal take-off re-usable launch vehicle would be faced with similar noise problems as the SST: sonic booms would also track these vehicles on the ground. The magnitude of this problem would be compounded if such a winged type of booster were required to remain within the atmosphere for extended periods, such as may be necessary to satisfy supersonic combustion ramjet (scramjet) or other air-breathing propulsion requirements. However, the vertically launched ballistic transport completely circumvents the sonic boom problem, although its rocket engines generate a less objectionable noise (of a completely different nature), aimed toward the immediate vicinity of the launch site.

During a typical ascent, the vertical take-off rocket would reach transonic velocity approximately 1 min. after lift-off, when it has acquired an altitude of 25,000 ft (7·63 km.) At this relatively low altitude, as expected, a Mach-1 shock wave would be impinged on the nose of the vehicle. However, the flight path angle would be a mere 10° from the vertical with the propagated sonic boom travelling *away* from the ground, rather than parallel to it. Accordingly, the acoustic energy of the boom is dissipated or refracted by high-altitude atmospheric winds and temperature gradients. Consequently, no boom at all reaches the ground, even at the launch pad directly beneath the vehicle. The sonic boom would not be heard even in adverse weather conditions, in the presence of low clouds, which usually tend to focus or amplify noise. Normally the vehicle would reach a speed of Mach 3 (three times the speed of sound) approximately 110 sec. after lift-off at an altitude of about 75,000 ft (22·9 km.). Under these conditions, the vehicle has already begun to veer in the direction of its destination. On the re-entry leg of the ballistic trajectory the rocket is beginning to approach the level flight altitude of the SST. However, the rarefied atmosphere at this altitude will tend to inhibit sound transmission. More significantly, the velocity and direction of the vehicle with its attached pressure wave will still be moving away from the Earth, even at the corresponding flight path angle.

Operational terminals for commercial rockets must be located sufficiently far away from populated areas to avoid engine noise complaints. And yet, these spaceports must be near enough to urban centres in order not to mitigate the reduced-time advantage associated with transporting passengers and goods at rocket speeds. As an illustration, the city centre of Cocoa Beach, Florida, is located a mere 18 miles (29 km.) from the Saturn 5 launch complex at Cape Kennedy. During any particular space launch, only an innocuous low-intensity rumble is heard by Cocoa Beach residents. Separation distances of this magnitude between spaceports and cities appear to be completely acceptable, provided that the thrust level of the operating commercial rockets do not exceed the 7·5 million lb thrust of Saturn 5.

The engine noise which would be heard during landing of a VTOVL rocket will be at a much diminished level than at take-off. The thrust magnitude necessary for terminal velocity cancellation and hover prior to touch-down is greatly reduced. This is so because the vehicle has consumed the propellants, which comprise 90 per cent of its lift-off weight, while in transit to its antipodal destination. Hence, only 10 per cent of the initial thrust required at launch is needed during a typical landing manoeuvre. The resulting noise from the rocket engine would be reduced in accordance with the decreased thrust level.

Even today, road access to major airports is becoming progressively more congested and increasingly intolerable to the travelling public. Helicopter flights, which now connect airport terminals to major hotels in cities and suburban locations, have become extremely popular and enjoy impressive financial success. Unquestionably VTOL aircraft or helicopters would again prove most adequate for connecting the 20 miles (32·2 km.) between future spaceports and adjacent major cities. If suitable unpopulated areas were not available for construction of spaceports, off-shore landing and launching facilities would be logical alternatives.

It is generally believed that space-travel requires enormous amounts of propulsive energy. This is a gross popular misconception, for the following reasons. A commercial airliner such as the DC-8 cruises at a lift-to-drag (L/D) ratio of 16. It can travel the 2,500 miles (4,000 km.) from New York to Los Angeles in about 5 hr. The L/D ratio signifies that the engines are applying a thrust equal to one-sixteenth of the aircraft weight for the entire flight duration. If, somehow, the energy from the aircraft engines could be released in the absence of the Earth's gravitational field and atmospheric drag, the vehicle would have accelerated at $\frac{1}{16} g$, or 2·0 ft./sec.^{2} (0·61 m./sec.^{2}) for 18,000 sec. The aeroplane would have attained almost enough velocity, 36,000 ft/sec. (39,400 km./hr.), to escape from the Earth! Thus, a routine flight of only 1,740 miles (2,800 km.) by a commercial jetliner consumes energy (and fuel) with the same order of magnitude as is required for an orbital space transport, i.e. 25,000 ft/sec. (27,400 km./hr.). This is true essentially because aircraft must combat gravity and drag incessantly during their entire atmospheric flight. However, vertically launched rocket transports can overcome drag and gravity quickly, and therefore efficiently, during a very brief portion of their entire flight time. They will then coast unpowered for approximately 88 per cent of their total transit times to orbital or antipodal destinations.

Let us now turn our attention to that commodity, mail, which historically has led the trend to faster forms of transportation. It has been the prime mover behind the introduction of almost every new and unconventional type of vehicle. It might be appropriate, therefore, to consider mail as the initial cargo for transport rockets.

In 1968, the total annual volume of international airmail and air-freight, delivered from city-to-city around the world was 200 million ton-miles (292,000 million kg.-km.). This enormous traffic would justify even the most ambitious rocket programme, if no competing vehicles existed. Moreover, bearing in mind current predictions for an exploding world population, this traffic volume promises to increase sharply in the future. In view of the rocket's speed, it might be tempting to conclude that mail will, indeed, provide a large and flourishing demand for rocket transportation. However, such a singular application might initially require an international subsidy of perhaps $1,000 million per year. Moreover, much of the world's airmail 20 years from now will be handled by communications satellites, which will compete with the cargo rocket for the delivery of high-priority communications.

Studies of synchronous satellites indicate that one hour of video communication to any place in the world may eventually cost as little as $1,000 – and in that one hour, about 8,000 facsimile pages may be transmitted. The direct operating cost could be $0·012 per page. For this same cost, 20,000 teletyped pages each containing 5,000 pieces of information might be transmitted.

Surprisingly, the use of rockets for cargo transport was first demonstrated experimentally by an Austrian engineer, Friedrich Schmiedl, as long ago as 1931. He completed several mail-delivery flights over mountainous country between the Austrian towns of Schöckel and Radegund and Schöckel and Kumberg. His unique mail service using simple powder rockets achieved semi-official status before it was terminated in 1933 by the Schuschnigg authorities who apparently viewed the rocket as a potential weapon.

Further attempts at establishing rocket mail services were made by Gerhard Zucker in Germany and England. Experiments were also made in India, France, and the United States. All these launches had ended by 1939, undoubtedly because of the impending war and preoccupation with the rocket's military potential. While rocket achievements have since fulfilled the wildest dreams of Konstantin Tsiolkovsky, Dr Robert Goddard, Professor Hermann Oberth, Robert Esnault-Pelterie, and other space pioneers, their *commercial* development has remained virtually stagnant. Commander Glauco Partel of Italy has used a patented hot-water rocket for mail-flight demonstrations, but only on an experimental scale.

The need to justify new forms of transport systems on economical grounds has been the major obstacle to more rapid progress. Within living memory, the rocket failed to engender support in America, a fact dramatically illustrated by the phlegmatic indifference to Dr Goddard's first successful launching of liquid-propellant rockets in the 1920s. Not until after World War II was the enormous potential of the rocket pursued in the United States. By that time, Germany, and later the Soviet Union, had invested huge sums in research and development.

While outwardly it appears prudent and judicious to place a 'price tag' on revolutionary new developments, it must be kept in mind that technological breakthroughs can drastically alter the balance of power among nations, a factor which defies economic assessment.

Although we should always be realistic in our forecasts, allowance must be made for the fact that science and technology today are moving at a pace more rapid than experts dared to predict even a few years ago. Consider the following startling facts: more than 90 per cent of all professionally trained engineers and scientists who have ever lived are alive today; more than 50 per cent of all research and development conducted throughout the history of human civilization has taken place in the last decade; and more than 50 per cent of man's total store of knowledge, in all fields, has been acquired during the last two decades. Where does this lead mankind in future technological accomplishment?

In the field of transportation, the first large-scale rocket transport would probably be used for unmanned cargo delivery long before it could be accepted for passengers. The first terrestrial cargo would most likely be military supplies, whereas orbital cargo would undoubtedly be equipment for the construction of a large space station, or for extended lunar-base operations, or for eventual manned planetary exploration. Now let us see how such a cargo rocket might be designed.

In 1962, the National Aeronautics and Space Administration placed a $500,000 contract for a 'Post-Saturn Launch Vehicle Study' with US Industry. As reflected in its title, the study was directed towards identification of the characteristics and operating mode of the next generation of launch vehicle, after Saturn. This two-year technical study, directed and managed for a California aerospace firm by one of the authors, resulted in an extremely attractive orbital cargo delivery system. The vehicle which was conceived during this exhaustive study was considered of such promise that the US Government applied for two patents on its design. In July 1965, a configuration patent (No. 201,773) was obtained, and in January 1967, a detail design patent (No. 3,295,790) was awarded to the space agency which funded the original research work. Both of these patents cite one of the authors as inventor of the vehicle design. Although there currently exist no firm plans for development of the 'Recoverable Single-Stage Spacecraft Booster', this configuration can serve to provide some insight into what the future may hold, perhaps more perceptively than any of the other concepts discussed.

To the best of the authors' knowledge, this is the only existing US patent for a re-usable type of launch vehicle. This conceptual freight rocket was given the name ROMBUS, an acronym for Reusable Orbital Module-Booster and Utility Shuttle. Since ROMBUS was designed for future weight-lifting assignments to orbit, its size is enormous by comparison with the SASSTO/ SARRA vehicle of the previous chapter. ROMBUS would weigh 14 million lb (6·35 million kg.) including payload, and its engines would generate 18 million lb (8·20 million kg.) of thrust at lift-off from Cape Kennedy. But our size perspective is always a purely relative matter. When the first DC-3 was rolled out, little more than 30 years ago, people's reactions were almost unanimous: 'Fantastic.' 'The thing's too big.' 'It'll never fly!' The word 'fantastic' could also be applied to the capabilities of ROMBUS.

This single-stage space cargo carrier could orbit a payload of 400 to 500 tons (362,000 to 453,000 kg.), return to Earth for a touch-down on land, and be re-used perhaps a hundred times. The highly manoeuvrable spaceship would eliminate the use of cumbersome balloon structures for re-entry, or the complications of parachutes and an ocean recovery. It would combine compactness and re-usability to offer a high degree of reliability, slashing the cost of orbiting payloads to a fraction of those demonstrated by the least expensive of today's expendable boosters. ROMBUS could be developed by the mid 1980s. It would not be unreasonable to expect each vehicle to be launched and re-used from 20 to 100 times during a 10-year operational programme. Not only would this offer cost-cutting advantages over expendable rockets, but it also would facilitate trouble-shooting and allow technical problems to be solved after substantially fewer flights.

Average turn-round time for the one-stage ROMBUS would be only one and a half weeks, considerably less than that required for recovery and refurbishment of competitive two-stage re-usable vehicle concepts. ROMBUS would be lighter and more compact than designs for other future space boosters, which have been or are now on the drawing-boards. Key to its versatility would be a multi-purpose plug-nozzle engine, an essential requirement for the concept, because conventional bell-nozzle engines could not survive the aerodynamic heating during base-first re-entry. The ascent propulsion system would also be used for orbit injection and rejection, and for landing retro-thrust. Circulation of liquid hydrogen fuel would cool the re-entry body.

Eight detachable liquid hydrogen propellant tanks would be strapped around the tapered vehicle during the initial boost. Once expended, the tanks would be jettisoned to improve flight performance and manœuvrability during recovery. The tanks would be constructed of low-cost throw-away material, or they could be eased back to Earth by parachute. ROMBUS would be compact by comparison with most space vehicles with similar payload capability which have been studied in the past. Its overall recovered height is only 95 ft (29 m.) and the base diameter 80 ft (24 m.). This basic structure, stripped of its payload and strap-on tanks – the form it would have when descending from orbit – would weigh approximately 500,000 lb (227,000 kg.).

ROMBUS would land on Earth in a manner similar to the Apollo lunar-landing technique, descending aft-end first, with the large, flat base increasing drag during re-entry. Landing would be accomplished by using the retro-thrust of the main engine, and by a final hovering manœuvre near the Earth's surface, during which four landing legs would be extended. The scheme is illustrated on pages 72–73.

By a significant margin, re-usability appears to be the most desirable feature for the next generation of launch vehicle. Only with a re-usable system can the operating cost of existing expendable vehicles be significantly reduced. Anticipated costs of $250 per lb ($550 per kg.) to orbit for the least expensive of today's operational boosters could possibly be trimmed to $25 per lb ($55 per kg.) for ROMBUS with only 20 re-uses. Toward the end of a 10-year operational period, 100 re-uses could reduce the cost to $10 per lb ($22 per kg.), or less.

This cost reduction would result from averaging the initial purchase of the vehicle over a large number of flights. Such operations would then be similar to commercial airlines, where the operating cost includes only fuel and flight expenditures. Indeed, no medium of transportation can long survive the extravagance of using the carrier vehicle once only. Over the years to come, long-range economy, and not immediate space-spectaculars, must establish a firm superiority.

ROMBUS would be correctly sized for its basic orbital mission, and perhaps for delivery of military cargo and troops (Chapter Seven) on Earth. The commercial vehicle for conveying travellers and their baggage from one point on Earth to another could be a smaller version of the same basic design.

CHAPTER SIX

THE BALLISTIC PASSENGER TRANSPORT

Suppose, for instance, that a diplomat presenting a speech on foreign policy in the 1990s, opened his remarks to a London audience with these words: 'Gentlemen, as I said during my talk in Tokyo tomorrow. . . .' Fantastic? It certainly sounds fantastic, that a man could quote today from a talk he had already given tomorrow, on the other side of the globe. But it is not impossible. It is not even improbable! The passenger vehicle that could sustain such a remark already is fairly well defined. It is an orbital/global rocket transport that could take you anywhere on Earth in less than 45 min. This passenger rocket, which is called Pegasus, could travel the 6,000 miles (7,000 km.) from London to Tokyo in 34 min. Pegasus would make it possible to leave London on Monday, conduct business in Tokyo on Tuesday, and arrive back in London on Monday, before – according to the calendar – you had kept your appointments in Tokyo.

During the next decade, more than 99 per cent of all air passengers will be content to travel on subsonic aircraft. But we must plan for the Pegasus age. To deny its coming would be to deny progress. We must plan for it within the framework of today's economic and technical realities, and with an eye to the more immediate needs of future world travel. Perhaps, after the supersonic transports, will come the hypersonic transports at six, seven, ten times the speed of sound, using new types of engines with hydrogen for fuel; also will come more exotic propulsion techniques, including use of nuclear energy and electrically charged particles. And the rocket transport will come, too! To believe otherwise is to risk putting one's self in the same position as those who, only yesterday, dismissed space-travel as science-fiction.

In fact, we already have the technological capability to turn the Pegasus concept into a reality. And according to a formula developed by our educators, our total store of knowledge will grow as much in the next ten years as it did during the first 1,750 years of our present calendar.

Airlines have already confirmed their belief in the future by placing orders for over $3,000 million worth of new aircraft, with *each* of the three major US airframe manufacturers. How much faith have they expressed in the probability of rocket commerce? William Allen Patterson, the man who built United Air Lines into its position of US dominance, retired in 1965 from his position of Board Chairman. And, on retiring, he told a reporter: 'Commercial traffic by rocket is coming for sure. I can't give you a date, but some day you'll fly by rocket from New York to Manila in 45 minutes at 17,000 miles an hour, perhaps 70 miles above the Earth.'

The late Grant McConachie, former president of Canadian Pacific Airlines, once commented that the future of high-speed passenger travel rests on airships operated on principles similar to those now used by astronauts' launch vehicles. Moreover, the distinguished space-lawyer, Andrew G. Haley, former president of the International Astronautical Federation, once stated:

> An area most often overlooked, namely, the advent of rocket transportation from point-to-point on the Earth's surface, will achieve great impetus. Within decades we will have rocket communications between distant points such as Moscow and New York, Melbourne and London, and so on. This new form of transportation will create vast international problems and vast new requirements for facilities. The great central pine-laden plateau of New Jersey will be cleared to become an immense landing and launching field for rocket ships. From here cargo and human beings will be transported to London in a half hour and to Moscow in 45 minutes. This type of transportation is quite inevitable.

The trends of the past lead us inevitably to one conclusion for the future. Just as the throw-away space launch vehicles of today were a logical progression from the expendable ICBMs of yesterday, a new class of carriers for high-income passengers is certain to evolve from the re-usable booster of tomorrow. Evolution of the Pegasus rocket transport system has been based on the premise that vehicle survival of atmospheric penetration will one day become commonplace. In that event, a re-usable booster with a 100-ton (90,700 kg.) orbital cargo capability may initially be developed, and later adapted for ballistic surface-to-surface passenger delivery.

In a sense, Pegasus would be a one-fifth scale version of the ROMBUS booster discussed in the previous chapter. The SASSTO/SARRA vehicle of Chapter Four did not incorporate a disposable-tank feature, as did the lifting-body concept of Chapter Three. Similarly, Pegasus incorporates disposable tanks on a semi-ballistically recovered vehicle.

The payload compartment of such a vertical take-off and vertical-landing (VTOVL) orbital rocket could be converted to deliver 170 passengers plus 18 tons (16,300 kg.) of cargo to the most distant point on Earth within 45 min. A freighter version of the global transport would carry 37 tons (33,500 kg.) of cargo, while an all-passenger version of Pegasus would transport a total of 260 persons and baggage. All Pegasus-type vehicles would be controlled by a two-man crew.

At an average speed of 17,000 m.p.h. (27,400 km./hr.), the passengers need not be subjected to peak accelerations of more than 3 g during boost or atmospheric entry. The 3 g's, of course, refers to an acceleration force (or weight) that is three times greater than what we experience on the surface of the Earth, due to its gravitational field.

Such a transport could rocket medical personnel and emergency equipment to any disaster area on Earth via a ballistic flight path, in a fraction of the time required by the supersonic transports. Without doubt, Pegasus could be the most revolutionary advance in commercial transportation since the introduction of the aeroplane.

This global transport vehicle, utilizing many newly acquired techniques of spaceflight, could be operational by the mid-1980s. The vehicle could easily satisfy those commercial markets, which might develop in the next few decades, for transporting passengers to (and from) Earth-orbiting space stations. This type of rocket-powered transport, operating at hypersonic speeds, is an extremely promising method of travelling outside Earth's atmosphere, where drag and prolonged aerodynamic heating are nonexistent. Excessive heating results when fast-flying vehicles travel through the lower, and more dense, portions of the atmosphere. Aerospace engineers have recently begun to wonder, 'Why bore a hole in the atmosphere? Why not get above it, "fly" to your destination, and then return through the atmosphere for a landing?'

By the 1980s, the probable state of international relations may be such that all nations will need the capability to make immediate, direct diplomatic contact with other countries. Time is one of man's most precious commodities; undoubtedly, future heads of state, executives, scientists, engineers, doctors, patients, professionals, and others in the 1980 era will need to travel at faster speeds than are currently provided by the supersonic transport.

Today, the international engineering community looks forward with confidence to man's repeated landings on the Moon. Equally as thrilling is an 1,800 m.p.h. (2,900 km./hr.) flight in the supersonic transport. A brief technical deliberation on these two seemingly unrelated engineering accomplishments would suggest that perhaps the basic technology needed for one objective could also satisfy the requirements for the other. Clearly, if passengers can be rocketed the 240,000 miles (386,000 km.) to the Moon, they can be rocketed much more easily and safely for one-twentieth of that distance, or half-way around the globe.

Moreover, travel at sub-orbital speeds of 17,000 m.p.h. (27,400 km./hr.), instead of the 1,800 m.p.h. (2,900 km./hr.) of the SST, offers impressive reductions in transit time. Thus, while we investigate the use of airbreathing machines, propelled at speeds for which they are perhaps not too well adapted, we cannot afford to dismiss the rocket transport as a far-fetched, impractical pipe-dream. We must design today as if the next decade or two had already passed.

The Pegasus vehicle might also tap an entirely new commercial market. Just as today's 'jet set' hops over to the Riviera for the weekend, the well-heeled tourist of the future might catch a Pegasus orbit express for rendezvous with a space station and a sojourn with companions 300 miles above the cares of the world.

Comparing today's air service with Pegasus's speed, the current

22 hr. flight from New York to Bombay, with intermittent stops at London, Frankfurt, and Beirut, would be contrasted to a non-stop Pegasus trip over the same route in only 40 min. The SST would be just a small step in the direction of reducing transit time, whereas rocket-propelled vehicles would provide the *ultimate* in sub-orbital speed for transportation on Earth's surface.

The VTOVL rocket transport, or 'domesticated missile', conceivably could incorporate propulsion, guidance, and structural components which have been developed for the manned space programme, under far more severe operating environments than would be required for terrestrial travel.

The value of a high-capacity aerospace workhorse was demonstrated during the international crisis which precipitated the Berlin airlift, lasting from April 1948 to September 1949. During this 18-month period, some 2·3 million tons (2,090 million kg.) of food and coal were airlifted by British and American planes into West Berlin.

The need for fast reaction time, as well as high-capacity transport capability, is re-emphasized from time to time during catastrophes such as the Alaskan earthquake, which occurred in March 1964. This disaster devastated a large portion of the runway at Anchorage International Airport, the nerve centre of Alaskan commercial aviation. Communications were in ruins. Tons of water, food, medical supplies, and field hospitals had to be airlifted immediately, and then distributed to the badly stricken areas south of Anchorage.

During the first three days of this emergency, military planes landed more than 300 tons (272,000 kg.) of supplies in Alaska. The largest single item was a 34,000 lb (15,500 kg.) gas-turbine for generation of electricity. Other heavy cargo included nine 25,000 lb (11,400 kg.) water purifiers, each of which could process 1,500 gal. (5,700 l.) of water each hour. In little more than a week, a single commercial airline had airlifted nearly 200 tons (181,000 kg.) of cargo.

This operation was truly an amazing performance for subsonic transport vehicles. However, the Pegasus vehicle, as presently envisioned, would be capable of delivering 170 medical personnel plus 18 tons (16,300 kg.) of emergency equipment from the

Western Test Range (WTR) on the Pacific Coast of the United States to Anchorage, Alaska, in just 17 min., despite the condition of the airfield runways upon arrival.

For this same flight, the SST requires over an hour. Existing subsonic turbojet aircraft, on the other hand, required 3 hr. to travel that portion of the flight just from Seattle, Washington, to Anchorage, Alaska. Thus, the speed and associated tonnage rate possible with the Pegasus rocket transport would open new vistas in disaster relief, including the reduction or elimination of destructive after-effects.

Since 1960, both the number of space vehicles launched, and the size of the payloads they carried, have grown steadily. Extrapolation of accomplishments to date suggest that activity in near space will continue to grow until we should be able to handle space launchings on a routine basis in the not-too-distant future.

During the first decade of the space age, launch vehicle developments had been predicated on a pattern which was largely influenced by the antecedent missile-launching technology. Although this pattern of development provided a timely booster capability which was consistent with the expedient and exploratory nature of the Space Age, many engineers believe that marked improvements in launch vehicles will be required to allow effective exploration of space in an economical manner.

Only recently has it appeared possible that both the orbital and global markets may be served by a single transport system. However, the traffic volume for city-to-city markets would exceed, by several orders of magnitude, that predicted for orbital traffic; thus, the terrestrial market's effect on the operational costs for orbital usage, could be profound. Only a highly ambitious space exploration programme can, by itself, justify the initial investment required for development of the Pegasus vehicle. Conversely, if a highly versatile orbital/global rocket transport existed in operational status, then undoubtedly we should find innumerable 'unheard-of' uses for such a vehicle.

Historically, the introduction of each new transportation system has stimulated people to travel more often, and to greater distances. It was true for the stage-coach, ocean liner, train, automobile, and propeller-driven aircraft. Since October 1958, when the subsonic jet was put into service for US–European flights, the number of transatlantic passengers has increased fourfold and air cargo tonnage tenfold. Emergence of the rocket transport upon the scene will unquestionably stimulate similar consequences, in the decades ahead.

But the correct sizing of this radically new rocket transport, is a factor of enormous importance. Its mandatory versatility feature will be strongly affected by the vehicle's size. For the sake of illustration, an initial orbital payload has been adopted which is comparable to that of the Saturn 5 vehicle. The ability to scale-down Pegasus to an even smaller size, or to off-load propellants when smaller-payload missions were required, was also maintained as a major objective. A Saturn 5-size vehicle which can be used more than once could perform post-Apollo missions with significantly improved economy.

Booster re-usability, single-stage-to-orbit capability, and land recovery emerged during the extensive Pegasus study as the predominant design and operational features necessary for any efficient rocket transport device. The Pegasus global transport was configured as a truncated cone, having a height of 114 ft (34·8 m.), a payload diameter of 33 ft (10 m.), a base diameter of 50 ft (15·2 m.), a gross weight of 3·34 million lb (1·52 million kg.) and a thrust of 4·2 million lb (1·91 million kg.). The basic design is shown on pages 74–75.

Although this chapter is primarily devoted to a discussion of the passenger transport, it is the all-cargo version of this vehicle that might find itself available at a particular point in time, concurrent with the existence of an airfreight market requirement. Except for the cheaply constructed throw-away fuel tanks, the single-stage-to-orbit Pegasus booster would be a completely re-usable system. Incorporation of advanced technology into the orbital version of Pegasus could reduce its overall length to 162 ft (49·4 m.) less than the Saturn 5 launch vehicle, with a corresponding reduction in gross weight of 2·66 million lb (1·21 million kg.). The most significant aspect of this potential weight reduction would be the corresponding decrease in lift-off thrust, and the associated reduction of adverse acoustic effects on personnel and structures. Pegasus would require about half the thrust of Saturn 5 and the passenger version would be one-third as tall as Saturn 5. Yet each vehicle would perform approximately the same orbital mission; Pegasus would inject a 200,000 lb (90,800 kg.) payload into a 300-nautical-mile (558 km.) orbit as compared with Saturn 5's ability to deliver 220,000 lb (100,000 kg.) to the same orbital altitude.

One should re-emphasize that Pegasus is a one-stage-to-orbit, disposable-tank vehicle employing liquid oxygen and liquid hydrogen as propellants, and an advanced engine. Eight cylindrical external tanks (used for liquid hydrogen fuel only) would be dropped during ascent to orbit. After payload separation in orbit, the main vehicle would be de-orbited by the same rocket engine used for ascent. All propellants needed for orbital injection, de-orbiting, and landing would be contained within spherical tanks located in the main body of the vehicle.

Drag deceleration during atmospheric entry would be accomplished by arranging the attitude of the craft so that it would re-enter with its blunt base in the forward position. Aerodynamic heating of the blunt entry nose in this base-first attitude would be controlled by circulating liquid hydrogen, in much the same manner as conventional bell nozzles are cooled during engine operation. It has been resolved that this plug nozzle must be designed to cool 43 times as much heat flux from engine exhaust during ascent as from aerodynamic heating during entry.

After terminal velocity is reached by the entry body, the main engines would be reignited to provide retro-thrust; the vehicle then would settle down on its four-legged landing gear. Hence, land recovery on Earth would exploit the expensive technology already developed and perfected for the Apollo manned lunar landing.

The Pegasus centre-body would be sized for a 33 ft (10 m.) diameter, in order to accommodate the Saturn S-II stage, or the S-IVB stage with an Apollo-type payload. In this manner, the re-usable vehicle would be provided with sufficient flexibility to perform future Saturn 5 missions with greatly reduced cost. The Pegasus vehicle is based on many radical departures from present conventional booster design. The principal advantage of the disposable tank feature is the improved performance which can be acquired during powered ascent by virtue of dropping off inert structure as soon as it is no longer needed. Hence, this unnecessary mass does not have to be accelerated to orbital velocity, at the expense of additional propellant.

Perhaps the recovery consideration is equally as important as the performance-improvement aspect. The entry manœuvre can be performed far more effectively when a large portion of the airframe (mass and volume) has been jettisoned along the way, or left in orbit.

But why single-stage-to-orbit? Staging is an important principle of space transportation systems, especially contemporary ones. The basic principle of staging is that those components of the vehicle which have fulfilled their usefulness are jettisoned, thereby reducing the undesirable mass. A conventional two-stage vehicle, for instance, has two propulsion systems, one for each stage. The first stage accelerates the second stage with its payload, until the fuel in the first stage is expended. Then the first stage is discarded or left behind, and the second stage adds the speed needed to complete the orbital mission. Sometimes, as with Pegasus, merely the tanks would be jettisoned once their propellant had been used. In other cases, as with the Atlas booster, the heavy, high-thrust engines needed for take-off of the fully fuelled vehicle may be jettisoned, allowing smaller 'sustainer' engines to boost the payload the remainder of the way.

While performance considerations clearly dictate multiple stages, other considerations, such as re-usability, favour a single stage. The soft-landing and retrieval of the individual stages of a multi-stage rocket which have been strewn about the planet, and their return to the launch site to be re-used, constitute a difficult and costly transportation problem. In contrast, a single stage-to-orbit booster can remain in orbit until the time is right for it to return from space to the immediate vicinity of the launch site. In other words, the operational advantages of a single-stage booster overshadow the performance advantages of a multi-stage conventional booster.

A recent reliability study indicates that hot-firing checkout of all engines, during the brief hold-down period on the launch pad prior to launch release, circumvents the large majority of engine malfunctions. In the past most engine malfunctions have occurred at, or shortly after, engine ignition. Additional reliability can be gained by installing one more rocket engine than is absolutely necessary. In this manner, one redundant engine can fail without catastrophic results. This single-engine-out capability would avoid most of the remaining engine malfunctions which occur during engine operation. Such a design philosophy suggests that a large number of small engines is more desirable than one larger combustion chamber. Moreover, the smaller engine modules are simpler and less costly to develop. Clustering a large number of main-engine modules poses no technical problems, as demonstrated by the success of the 20-chamber Vostok booster. The Pegasus propulsion system has 16 combustion chambers, each of which produce 263,000 lb (119,000 kg.) of thrust at lift-off.

The upper end of Pegasus would contain a four-decked passenger area, each level fitted with 43 individual couches, on which travellers would ride during their brief flight through space. During the few minutes of weightless flight, passengers would be constrained by belts attached to the couches. On a ballistic Pegasus mission the acceleration vector during ascent, and the deceleration vector during descent, will be in the same direction with respect to the passenger; i.e. acceleration loads would be distributed by the couch to the passenger's back at both ends of the journey. By comparison, during a glide-type re-entry, the deceleration force is in the opposite direction, resulting in what is called an 'eyeballs-out' condition. Besides subjecting the human body to severe discomfort, this condition can impair the crew's visibility and their ability to cope with an unexpected emergency.

Prior to lift-off, internal access stairwells would interconnect the four decks of Pegasus for emergency egress. Three external entry doors are located at each of the four deck levels for rapid loading and unloading of passengers. To diminish the noise effect on personnel, the payload compartment would be constructed of a double-wall acoustic-damping material. Prior to loading of passengers, the vehicle would be completely checked out, and the propellant tanks filled. Constant topping would ensure that the propellant in the tanks was at the proper level, before take-off.

Passengers would enter the vehicle through a mobile tower

which incorporates a number of elevators for lifting the travellers from ground level, some 60 ft (18·3 m.) to the passenger compartment. Three ramps, located between the external hydrogen tanks, service the entry doors at each of the four deck levels of the vehicle payload. During atmospheric entry, these door openings are located on the upper side of the vehicle, thus keeping the highly heated underside free of structural openings and discontinuities.

Of the 3·3 million lb (1·5 million kg.) gross weight, the Pegasus vehicle structural weight and residual propellant amounts to 326,000 lb (148,000 kg.). Approximately 20 per cent of this total inert weight can be charged directly to the recovery system, which includes the liquid hydrogen for cooling the plug nozzle heat shield while it is taking the brunt of frictional heating. Also included are the propellants for providing reverse thrust and hover capability. It is particularly significant that an inert mass equivalent to the recovery system is jettisoned when the eight liquid hydrogen tanks are discarded. The first group of four tanks is jettisoned about 130 sec. after lift-off, when the vehicle has passed through the regime of maximum dynamic pressure. The next pair of diametrically opposed tanks is discarded about two minutes later, and the last pair 6 min. after lift-off, following shut-down of the main engines.

When the vehicle is launched from a coastal spaceport, the throw-away hydrogen tanks fall harmlessly into the sea. However, if a launch site were required near an inland city such as Paris, Berlin, or Chicago, these circumstances would demand that no disposable tanks or expendable stages be incorporated into the vehicle design to avoid debris impacting a densely populated area. If this requirement should prevail, then the SASSTO-type of single-stage vehicle – without disposable tanks – might be the solution. The SASSTO type of terrestrial transport can be launched in any direction from a continental interior at the penalty of a somewhat-reduced performance.

Analytical results to date indicate that, in terms of increased payload, the technique of disposable tanks during flight, more than compensates for the recovery system weight penalty. In contrast to this fact, the control fins of Pegasus weigh more than half of the centre-body weight. For this reason, the offset centre of gravity and propulsive roll-control scheme used by SASSTO may appear to be a more efficient technique for obtaining manœuvrability than either fins or wings.

In spite of the above shortcomings, with some operational modifications, Pegasus may still prove to be 'the only way to fly'. As a combined manœuvrable spacecraft and booster, it offers an enormously improved mass ratio over winged or fin-controlled devices. It could retain the attractive feature of returning – in a backward re-entry posture to a preselected ground site – the single-stage booster with attached spacecraft or integral pressure cabin. A recently disclosed scheme, which was patented by two aerospace engineers from United Aircraft Corporation, suggests that Pegasus could avoid the objectionable hazards associated with discarding the circumferentially mounted external tanks and, furthermore, avoid the need for heavy control fins required only during re-entry. The eight cylindrical fuel tanks could be retained on the entry vehicle, and hinged outwards after re-entry to provide a means of modifying the descent path in the manner of drag brakes and rudders. The tanks hinge at the heat shield end opening out radially by means of a linkage mechanism. This scheme, mentioned briefly in Chapter Three, is illustrated on page 82.

To continue with the basic Pegasus design concept: for long-range missions – such as flying non-stop the 11,530 miles (18,600 km.) from Rio De Janeiro to Tokyo – the vehicle would be fully loaded with propellants. With the payload weight kept constant, propellants would be off-loaded (prior to lift-off) for shorter-range missions. Accordingly, a mission from London to New York would necessitate propellant tanks only 56 per cent full. The engines would be throttled at lift-off to maintain a constant thrust-to-weight ratio of 1·25, regardless of the vehicle gross weight. A rocket transport such as Pegasus, which is designed with detachable tanks, can be readily adapted for off-loaded missions merely by neglecting to install some of the external cylindrical hydrogen tanks. The internal spherical oxygen tank would simply not be filled to maximum capacity. On the other hand, with the propellant tanks fully loaded, the payload capability could be increased substantially for shorter distances.

It should be noted that neither the supersonic transport nor the subsonic jet possess the extensive range capability of a Pegasus vehicle. Assuming that the supersonic transport could travel the 10,100 miles (16,300 km.) from Rome to Sydney without stopping to refuel, its flight duration would be seven times as long as that required by Pegasus. The subsonic jet transport would require a travel time approximately 20 times greater. However, even an SST with a 4,000 mile (6,440 km.) maximum range, would have to stop at least twice along the way. Each stop will probably consume 30 to 45 min. for landing, refuelling-reloading, and take-off. In the total period of time the aircraft is on the ground, the rocket transport could accomplish both legs of the entire round trip. During a typical maximum-range Pegasus mission, booster burn-out would occur approximately 6 min. after lift-off, at an altitude of 70 nautical miles (130 km.). The vehicle would coast for an additional 12 min. reaching its apogee at 125 nautical miles (233 km.). The vehicle will descend for some 13 min. after apogee condition to start the entry portion of the flight profile, when it again approaches the edge of the atmosphere at an altitude of approximately 66 nautical miles (123 km.). The atmospheric entry phase is accomplished in 14 min.; hence, 55 per cent of the 45 min. flight time is spent above the atmosphere. The reaction control system will orient Pegasus into the required 49° nose-up attitude, prior to entry.

At lift-off, due to the ratio of engine thrust to gross weight, the vehicle would accelerate at 1·25 g. As propellant is consumed during powered flight, the engines would be progressively throttled to control the acceleration on the passengers. This deep-throttling condition is maintained throughout ascent, until main engine cut-off. During re-entry, after drag has completely cancelled the horizontal component of velocity, and the vehicle has reached a 'stalling' condition, the attitude control system will rotate the vehicle through the proper angle until the base is oriented directly downward. Four modules of the propulsion system are then re-started to nullify the vertical component of velocity. The vehicle has the design capability of hovering for 10 sec., pitching over 8°, and translating horizontally 1,000 ft (305 m.) in any direction, prior to settling down on the four extensible legs. Additionally, automatic checkout computers would be incorporated on-board to minimize the time required for relaunch of Pegasus on its next passenger-carrying mission.

During a normal ascent, Pegasus would rise almost vertically for about 70 sec. In the event of an engine malfunction, or any other emergency-abort condition, the eight external tanks, still full of volatile liquid hydrogen, can immediately be separated and jettisoned at sea (page 79). The major portion of the liquid oxygen would be pumped overboard from the internal spherical tank, through the turbine discharge port located in the centre of the plug nozzle. Ample propellant would be automatically retained on-board to provide sufficient retro-thrust for a soft-landing at sea. Because of this design feature, a rocket-powered VTOVL which can use an entire ocean or a small patch of unprepared terrain as its emergency landing site, might prove to be inherently safer than a jet aircraft. If trouble develops during an aircraft take-off, it must reach a particular airport with a sufficiently long runway for an emergency landing.

After propellants are dumped during an aborted Pegasus flight, four expandable-structure spheres would automatically be inflated from under the foot-pads. These spherical 'pontoons' provide hydrostatic buoyancy to the entire vehicle, after it alights on the ocean. Since very few engine modules are required to brake the empty vehicle, four segments between the landing legs would be automatically selected. During this emergency recovery mode, after settling on the ocean, the vehicle would be towed back to port. Numerous surface vessels and tow lines will stabilize the vehicle against adverse wind effects during the retrieval process. Unquestionably, this operation could prove to be a considerably 'rough' trip for the passengers returning to the coastal spaceport, depending on the magnitude of existing ocean swells. The travellers might arrive somewhat bilious, but alive, nonetheless.

A pressurized two-man crew compartment would be installed within the Pegasus centre-body, above the spherical liquid oxygen tank. The crew would enter this compartment by way of an external door and an internal access ramp, and then through an airlock. The airlock into the crew compartment would provide mission flexibility, allowing the crew to participate in extra vehicular activity (EVA) on orbital missions. On terrestrial missions, redirection capability could be incorporated into the on-board computer which controls vehicle guidance to pre-determined destinations. The crew would be provided with manual over-ride of this computer.

There is a heat shield below the external bulge of the crew compartment to protect the windows from excessive heating during entry. This heat shield is jettisoned after entry, just prior to the terminal-retro phase. The pilot and co-pilot can then look downward through the windows on the external bulge of their pressurized compartment. This gives them an unobstructed view for accurately pin-pointing the touch-down location at an inter-continental spaceport. After re-entry, four of the available 16 engine modules are ignited in a throttled mode, at an altitude of 2,500 ft (763 m.), to provide reverse thrust for terminal velocity cancellation. At reignition, only 610,000 lb (278,000 kg.) of total thrust is required to produce 2 g deceleration. The retro-thrust of these engines is progressively diminished for 12 sec.; they then produce 305,000 lb (139,000 kg.) of total thrust, to precisely balance the recovered weight. Roll control during this phase is provided by the secondary attitude-control system. Of the 16 individual thrust chambers, only one group of four modules need be automatically selected for operation during this manœuvre. Accordingly, extensive engine redundancy and its associated improved mission reliability, are provided at no additional weight penalty. After the hover manœuvre, the engines are automatically cut off when the landing legs are compressed upon touch-down.

For locating the predetermined landing site, Pegasus would contain a guidance system and electronic brain similar to the one used in the Ranger and Surveyor programme. The last few Rangers impacted their intended lunar destinations within 3 miles (4·8 km.) to 20 miles (32 km.). The vertically soft-landed Surveyors also travelled 20 times as far as Pegasus is expected to on Earth, and pin-pointed their lunar target locations with accuracy comparable to Ranger. Gemini and Apollo atmospheric entry vehicles have delivered their passengers within miss distances of 0·5 miles (0·8 km.) to 4·0 miles (6·4 km.) of their preselected ocean-recovery points. Although they were recovered from Earth orbit, these manned vehicles also use the lifting ballistic re-entry technique of Pegasus. The Apollo 8 capsule landed in the Pacific within 4 miles (6·4 km.) of the carrier USS *Yorktown*, after returning from 237,000 miles (382,000 km.) at near escape velocity. Accordingly, it is estimated that Pegasus would require a prepared elliptical landing area no larger than 1 mile (1·6 km.) wide, by 2 miles (3·2 km.) long at the spaceport. For additional safety precautions, an uninhabited, unpaved, elliptical buffer zone about 2 miles (3·2 km.) wide by 4 miles (6·4 km.) long could contain the Pegasus landing site. It is interesting to note that 10,000 ft (3,050 m.) runways at existing airports have required extensions to accommodate landings of the SST. Therefore, were it not for the noise problem, a rocket transport could easily operate out of available airports; as a minimal consideration, any existing airport could be used for Pegasus emergency landings.

But acceptance of the unconventional ballistic rocket, in spite of its unequalled advantages, will continue to meet with much psychological opposition, and even technical reluctance. Why? Merely because its appearance will evoke the inquiry: 'How can it fly like an aircraft, if it doesn't resemble one? . . . it has no wings!' At this point, an extremely valid analogy can be drawn. That the public would be hesitant to accept dramatic changes in the appearance of passenger transport vehicles – and radical departures from proven power generation systems – has been clearly demonstrated in the past. Many 'progressive' individuals refused to climb aboard an automobile, when it was first introduced. Moreover, the British vessel HMS *Sirius* crossed the Atlantic in 1838 propelled exclusively by the revolutionary new source of power – steam. However, wind-powered sails were not completely abandoned by reticent design engineers until 46 years later! And it may take almost that long, to convince the die-hards who still insist on subscribing to the 'winged-syndrome'!

How much would such a vehicle cost? It has been estimated that the orbital booster version of Pegasus would cost $3,000 million to develop, and the first flight item would cost $63 million. However, the rocket-bus would be 'cheaper by the dozen' – if four dozen were built, the unit cost would be down to $30 million.

Studies have shown that most business travellers fall into the following categories: professionals, owners and managers, salesmen, and skilled technicians. They may be diplomats, engineers, scientists, or specialists in construction, agriculture, manufacturing, sales and distribution, and government.

Now that the Space Age has provided us with the means to travel at tremendous velocities, can we identify any real need for this mode of transportation? Tens of thousands of people fly regularly to be present at more places in a given period of time – to consult, confer, inspect, decide, and lead in a manner impossible to accomplish from a distance, even with television. Is it reasonable to suppose that after another two decades of accelerated accumulation of knowledge in science, professions and business, it will be possible to convey specialized wisdom and critical solutions by any means other than direct personal contact? When the rocket transport is recognized as a means of communication rather than transportation, there will be no limit to the speed desired; and, as that speed is needed, it will be made available.

Perceptive observers have noted that historically there has appeared some new material or technique which has been a stimulus to human progress. Fire, writing, iron, the wheel, the sailing boat, steam power, electricity, dynamite, radio, and nuclear fission, have come in a sequence which, regardless of incidental military employment, closely parallels the progress of civilization.

History assures us that there is much more of the drama of man's achievements yet to unfold – but in what direction?

CHAPTER SEVEN

THE ROCKET AS A TROOP TRANSPORT

By this time it will be apparent that the optimum *size* for the rocket transport – to provide the multi-mission capability it needs to become economically viable – has yet to be defined. The re-usable vehicles already discussed range in gross weight from the 216,000 lb (98,000 kg.) of SASSTO to the 14 million lb (6·35 million kg.) of ROMBUS. Their corresponding orbital payload capabilities vary from 8,000 lb (3,629 kg.) to 800,000 lb (362,870 kg.). It is particularly relevant that the large-sized rockets can only be recovered ballistically in a vertical attitude; they involve such enormous touch-down weights that no sufficiently long runway exists anywhere in the world to permit a conventional winged landing.

Nevertheless, the decision of optimum size must await further rigorous technical study. The small SASSTO vehicle was correctly sized as a technology demonstration test-bed when used by itself, and for intermediate-sized orbital cargo delivery when boosted by additional Saturn 5 stages. The extremely large ROMBUS vehicle was correctly sized to deliver massive freight to Earth orbit for construction of a lunar base, or for eventual manned landings on the planets. The medium-sized Pegasus was designed primarily as a passenger transport to orbital resort hotels, or to antipodal Earth locations.

The size of a military rocket transport would depend on whether strategic necessities demanded delivery of a company-size complement, or a full battalion. The smaller versions of Ithacus (to give the military rocket transport a name) would look very much like the Pegasus carrier (of Chapter Six) in configuration and size. An all-cargo version of the junior-size Ithacus could transport 37 tons (33,500 kg.) of military support equipment or supplies; an all-passenger version of Ithacus Jr could transport 260 troops and their personal armament. These two Ithacus vehicles, when salvo-fired, could have a particularly unique military application. They can be launched from the deck of a converted aircraft carrier. For illustrative purposes, a vessel in the class of the nuclear-powered USS *Enterprise* was investigated (page 80).

It is of particular significance to note that small US aircraft carriers have already been used as mobile platforms for sounding-rocket launchings. Such an application for floating launch pads, offering the flexibility to dispatch rockets from anywhere in the world, suggests the dawn of a new era for the carrier, and adds a new dimension to military strategy. Just as the mobility of the submarine-launched Polaris missile makes its approach trajectory less predictable by the enemy than its silo-launched Minuteman counterpart, similarly will the rocket-propelled troop transport of the future be less vulnerable when dispatched from a mobile launch pad at sea. Additionally, an increase of about 25 per cent in payload capability can be realized when launching easterly, and taking full advantage of the Earth's rotational velocity. Synchronous equatorial orbits can then be established without the energy-consuming 'dog-leg' manœuvres necessary during launch from a Cape Kennedy latitude, into an orbit above the geographic equator.

The nuclear power plant of the USS *Enterprise* might ultimately serve to produce the liquid rocket propellants required by the booster, through electrolysis of sea-water. Only 10 years ago, the suggestion of dissociating the chemical bond between hydrogen and oxygen in water (H_2O) through an electrolytic process – using a nuclear reactor as the power source – would have been considered impracticable. However, very recently, the aerospace industry has developed such a portable self-contained reactor unit, which is being used today for precisely those purposes.

In the laboratory, 25·5 kilowatt-hours (Kw-Hr) of electrical power can convert 9 lb (or kg.) of water – of the free and plentiful variety – into 8 lb (or kg.) of oxygen, and 1 lb (or kg.) of hydrogen. In the US, home electricity costs about $0·0165 per Kw-Hr. Hence, approximately $0·42 of electricity can produce 9 lb of pro-pellants, at a cost of about $0·047 per lb. This cost is very com-parable to current costs (as specified in Chapter Five) for cryogenic propellants at a mixture ratio of 7 lb oxygen per lb of hydrogen.

However, the electrolysis of water would dissociate its two constituents into a gaseous state at atmospheric pressure and at 32° F (0° C). Additional electrical power, and further expense for a sub-cooling refrigeration cycle, would be required to liquefy the two separate gases. The liquid oxygen at −297° F (−183° C) and the liquid hydrogen at −423° F (−252° C) can then be stored in super-insulated tanks at low pressure.

Each launch of Ithacus Jr to its maximum range would consume 2·53 million lb (1·15 million kg.) of oxidizer, and 361,000 lb (164,000 kg.) of liquid hydrogen fuel. The reactor-driven turbines of the USS *Enterprise* could generate 224,000 kW. of electricity. Thus, by using half the generated power for this purpose, in four days, 389,000 gal. (1·47 million l.) of plain sea-water could be dissociated electrolytically to yield the required quantity of liquid hydrogen, plus 360,000 lb (164,000 kg.) more liquid oxygen than is required for a full tank-load in the rocket. The surplus oxygen could be used for the synthetic atmosphere which pressurizes the troop compartment of the junior-sized Ithacus.

The two Ithacus Jr rocket vehicles could be mounted on launch-platform extensions to the converted aircraft carrier main deck, fore and aft. These cantilevered extensions would be framed into the hull with diagonal supports. Blast-deflector plates would direct rocket engine exhaust away from the ship's hull, decks, and other structures. Local modification of the deck extremities would be required to protect the vessel from exhaust blast after vehicle lift-off. The exhaust-gas deflectors would be cooled by a deluge of abundant sea-water.

The Ithacus Jr rocket would be completely enclosed in an environment-controlled shelter, protecting the vehicle from weather and ocean spray. The shelter incorporates work platforms for maintenance and inspection, as well as provisions for personnel (and cargo) loading. Prior to vehicle launch, a collapsible door is opened, allowing the shelter to be retracted on rails installed on the main deck. The ship's superstructure, modified to withstand the high rocket-engine noise and potential blast hazard, could serve as a suitably protected observation post. A 'salvo'-type of launch, within seconds of each other may prove desirable when one rocket is loaded with troops and the other with support equipment. At the destination, the second vehicle could land within 2,000 ft (610 m.) of the first.

From the major conflicts of history, some bitter but conclusive lessons can be learned. The Trojan Horse; Hannibal's crossing of the Alps, and the retreat of Napoleon's infantry from Moscow, individually underscore the strategic necessity for effective transportation of troops and their support equipment. Each new era of human progress has brought with it an urgency for expanded payload capability to global ranges, augmented by a necessity for contracted time in transit. Without doubt, the Space Age, with its inherent energy demands for moving men and equipment during exploitation of the Moon and planets, will magnify these requirements exponentially.

Perhaps now, while the international technical community contemplates the design of an economically operating space vehicle, we might recognize that this decision with its implicit ramifications could revolutionize all previous transportation concepts.

The influence of a rocket-borne logistics transport might best be illustrated, in retrospect, by reference to the historical conflicts of World War II, in Europe and North Africa. Each major encounter would confirm the vital necessity for immediate transportation of supply equipment, in support of troop movements.

The record clearly shows that troop penetrations have depended on the ability to move logistics supplies at a speed commensurate with infantry advances. The victory at El Alamein, a turning-point of the war, may not have been so successful for the Allies had not Rommel and his Afrika Korps been forced to drop back in order to pick up their lagging supply lines.

The rocket method of supply delivery could circumvent the route restrictions imposed by available roads and traversable terrain. Moreover, the large manpower pool, otherwise required for overland transportation of supplies, could be freed for active engagement at the front lines. History has repeatedly reconfirmed the time-proven corollary that speed and mobility dictate military successes far more effectively than do sheer masses of armed troops.

Mobilization of millions of men and millions of tons of munitions prior to open hostilities can be an easily detectable tip-off to the enemy. When such a buildup of supplies can be performed within national continental boundaries, a higher probability of relative concealment can be acquired through disguise. Furthermore, instant strike capability from within a nation's own shores would preclude the necessity for world-wide overseas bases, with a correspondingly enormous reduction in defence costs.

Part of the large funds saved by eliminating overseas bases could instead be applied to development of the military rocket transport. It was precisely this point which General Wallace M. Greene Jr, then Commandant of the US Marine Corps, made to one of the authors in 1964. Of the rocket-borne troop transport, the visionary former member of the US Joint Chiefs of Staff, declared when he took office that 'the impact of this application of space technology on the projection of national military power is staggering to contemplate'. It was General Greene who conceived the idea that a full battalion of 1,200 marines might be loaded aboard huge rockets and fired off to trouble-spots in faraway lands.

US Army Major-General Andrew R. Lolli, the farsighted former Commander of the 28th NORAD Region, called the project a 'must' and expressed great enthusiasm for its potential, after a briefing on the subject. Retired General Bernard A. Schriever, former Commander of the US Air Force Systems Command, has commented that the day will come when we will be flying missiles over the US as we do jet planes today.

It was some 13 years ago that Dr Wernher von Braun first discussed the possibility of a troop carrier missile at a meeting of the Association of the United States Army. In Dr von Braun's concept a separate troop-carrying spacecraft would be launched by rocket from a base well behind front lines, and thrown on a ballistic path towards a target 500 miles (805 km.) away. Like Ithacus, Dr von Braun's troop-carrier would reverse ends in flight, and descend on the target at a safe speed controlled by rocket retro-thrust.

Once again, it appears that technologically sound ideas have a habit of being independently discovered, or reinvented, as the case may be. Nevertheless, the 1,200-passenger troop-carrier first proposed by General Greene would suggest a ROMBUS-sized derivative. Referred to as Ithacus Sr, this king-sized version could also be adapted to transport 132 tons (120,000 kg.) of cargo. The troop-carrying Ithacus Sr was configured as an overgrown artillery shell, with a height of 210 ft (64 m.), a payload diameter of 70 ft (21 m.), a base diameter of 80 ft (24 m.), and a gross weight of 14 million lb (6·4 million kg.). Ithacus is illustrated on page 76; the four-man crew compartment appears on page 77. Like its parent ROMBUS booster, it would develop a thrust of 18 million lb (8·2 million kg.). All eight disposable fuel tanks would each be 25 ft (7·6 m.) in diameter. The upper end of Ithacus Sr would contain a six-deck pressurized troop compartment, each level fitted with 200 individual couches.

The noise generated by a thrust level almost 2·5 times as great as Saturn 5, would present many new problems which have not been previously encountered in rocketry. Preliminary investigations indicate that acoustic fatigue may be one of the principal structural problems attendant with vehicles of this thrust magnitude. A design solution which applies to ROMBUS and Ithacus Sr has been suggested in the case of reflected acoustic energy from the launch complex. A concrete parabolic dish with a focal point approximately 520 ft (158 m.) above the bottom of the blast deflector supports the troop transport. With the vehicle on the launch pad, the noise source – the engine – is well below the focus of the parabola, causing the acoustic energy to be dispersed away from the longitudinal centre-line of the vehicle. After the launcher has ascended above the focus, the acoustic energy is concentrated at a point aft of the vehicle. Thus, the high concentration of noise and vibration reflected from the ground, is not directed toward the structural base of the vehicle. The special launch pad arrangement is shown on page 73.

Significantly, the 80 ft (24·4 m.) nozzle diameter of Ithacus Sr is only a valid size for vacuum conditions, when the nozzle is 'flowing full'. The equivalent nozzle diameter would be 25 ft (7·6 m.) at sea level because of the effect of atmospheric pressure on the exhaust flow. Preliminary design estimates indicate that the parabolic dish of the launch pad reflector should be approximately 20 nozzle diameters, or 500 ft (152 m.), across its edges and should extend approximately 60 ft (18 m.) below ground level.

It has been confirmed analytically that significant acoustic attenuation may be realized through the use of such a parabolic reflector.

Moreover, by filling the bottom of the reflector with water, additional damping may be acquired. The water will not retain a flat surface after engine ignition, but will take on an irregular quasi-parabolic shape under the influence of the exhaust and reflector. The irregular surface of the water generated by the exhaust gases will disperse and dissipate additional acoustic energy in the process. Similar noise-attenuation devices such as acoustic baffles and fine water-spray can be incorporated into the launch pad blast deflector, further damping the reflected noise to within tolerable limits. It is interesting that this design for a noise-diminishing launch pad was included in the previously discussed patent awarded to one of the authors.

Reliability is improved with an Ithacus single-stage vehicle, although an acknowledged performance and weight degradation is incurred. The absence of stage separation eliminates the need for ordnance devices and retro-rockets for interstage detachment. Altitude start of engines is avoided and all engines can be effectively checked out during the brief hold-down period on the launch pad. The absence of the stage-separation manœuvre, with its attendant tipover problems under dynamic pressures, results in large reliability gains. Without stage separation, less flight instrumentation and fewer malfunction detection systems are required.

On an optional delayed-action mission, the troop-carrying Ithacus could be launched into a polar orbit, and 'parked' there for 24 hr. During that period it would have unlimited capability of observing the entire surface of the globe, prior to selecting any particular target of interest. It should be pointed out, however, that this mode of operation will mitigate the original objective of instant-strike capability. Nevertheless, when this procedure is followed, the necessity of providing extensive cross-range velocity capability in the vehicle is minimized. In this manner, after 16 vehicle orbits, and one Earth revolution, the vehicle is in synchronous position to be recovered near its original launch site. At the appropriate moment, a ground signal could command the main engines to ignite, providing the velocity required for orbit ejection, and return to home base. Thus, land-recovery operations – or, indeed, the noisy launch operations – would prove far more acceptable at a military base than at the commercial airports proposed for certain horizontal-landing concepts.

Ground-transport devices, similar to the Saturn 5 'crawler', would handle the empty Ithacus vehicle at the military operational base. The 'crawler' is designed so it can move beneath the landed Ithacus, and support the vehicle near the engine attachments. The entire vehicle weight is then supported along the same high-strength structural load path which carries the engine thrust forces during boost. A drawing depicts Ithacus on the crawler device at a coastal pad (page 81).

The combustion chamber of Ithacus is comprised of 36 segments, each producing 500,000 lb (228,000 kg.) of thrust at sea level. The conceptual vehicle can then successfully perform its intended mission with six (to eight) engine segments inoperative during boost. The orbital injection, ejection, and terminal retro-thrust manœuvres can be accomplished by ignition of any four of the 36-engine segments. One turbo-pump was assumed to provide the required propellant flow rate for each pair of combustion chambers, with two turbo-pumps carried on board as fully-redundant units.

Regenerative cooling during re-entry is much more practical for a truly re-usable vehicle. Ablatant, which might have to be replaced after each flight, would also char and foul the annular engine throat. This fouling could result in a malfunction when the engine is later expected to restart for terminal retro-thrust prior to landing. Because the isentropic plug-nozzle engine must be regeneratively cooled during operation, it appears feasible to use this same method for cooling during re-entry. Since the engine is inoperative during the maximum-heating regime of re-entry, a gas generator could be used to run the on-board turbo-pump, which pressure-feeds the liquid hydrogen coolant. After cooling the centre-body, the hydrogen is fed through the engine injector and discharged overboard through the annular throat, helping to cool the combustion chamber in the process.

Unlike the Jules Verne notion that rocket-borne humans would be launched from the mouth of a cannon – thereby imposing

intolerable accelerations on the passengers – recent studies con-
clusively prove that launch and entry forces can be kept within
reasonable limits. Perhaps these limits would still prove unaccept-
able to the 'little old lady in tennis shoes', but certainly would not
be excessive for the average public. To associate the 2·5 to 3 g
predicted for Ithacus with more familiar conditions, the emergency braking system built into a hotel elevator will subject
passengers to 3 g while in a standing position – an extremely
uncomfortable posture for withstanding deceleration loads. The
arresting gear on an aircraft carrier deck subjects the pilot of the
landing aircraft to 4 g for a very brief period. Snatch loads associated with parachute deployment can subject paratroopers to a
short-term exposure as high as 15 g. By comparison, the deceleration level of Ithacus is no greater than that experienced 'just for
thrills' during a roller-coaster ride at many amusement parks.

During entry, the shock wave propagated from the Ithacus
blunt nose will protect the fin leading edges from severe heating
conditions. These fins were sized to allow containment of their
entire area within the outside envelope defined by the external
hydrogen tanks. Thus, high-velocity wind sheer gradients during boost would not be imposed directly on the fin surface,
thereby avoiding the otherwise severe destabilizing moments
which might result. Page 75 illustrates Pegasus during this mode
of re-entry.

In the event of a landing at remote, hostile, or land-locked
destinations, propellants could be supplied by ground vehicles,
providing that enemy action permitted such activity. After troop
deployment and refuelling, the vehicle could take off directly from
its landing legs. It would then make a short flight to the nearest
seacoast, where a ground transportation 'crawler' would lift the
empty vehicle and carry it to an awaiting barge (page 81). In
this manner, the enormous vehicle could be transported by
barge to a coastal spaceport for refurbishment and relaunch. On
flights of sufficient strategic importance, return of the vehicle
would have to be postponed until enemy action had diminished.
Although the size of the vehicle presents a large target for enemy
gunfire, its speed and brief flight time will tend to offset that
disadvantage. Clearly, during missions of less than maximum

range, unused propellant could be retained (for relaunch purposes) in the external tanks attached to the upper side of the
vehicle during re-entry.

The suggestion of launching a booster for even a short hop
without using a launch pad may, at first sight, appear somewhat
unrealistic. However, it should be remembered that the Apollo
mission makes use of precisely such a technique for the return trip
from the Moon. The lunar module is launched directly off its
four-legged support from the lunar surface. By incorporating
automatic checkout equipment – which also could be used for
Ithacus – the need for a launch crew *or launch pad* is completely
avoided. In time, perhaps, the launch complex which will be
required at the outset of the Ithacus operational missions may be
dispensed with, although it appears that *initial* take-offs will be
conducted from the unconventional launch pad illustrated on
page 73.

Ithacus, with its landing weight of 1·28 million lb (500,000 kg.)
has also been compared with three typical aircraft, which weigh
as much as 270,000 lb (123,000 kg.) at touch-down. During an
emergency landing, the Ithacus vehicle – even when only three
of its four legs are loaded on touch-down – can land on any type
of unprepared terrain except for quicksand or silt. In contrast,
a large bomber aircraft could not land on anything other than a
long runway situated upon hard rock.

In many past instances, where instant-strike capability was
required, squadrons of bomber aircraft have been kept airborne
around the clock. Under similar circumstances, Ithacus could be
maintained on standby-alert, ready to respond to a plea for help
from half a globe away. It may prove feasible to maintain Ithacus
in a state of instant readiness, with troops loaded on-board the
vehicle, prepared for immediate dispatch to a potential trouble
area.

Boil-off of the cryogenic propellants does not appear to be a
problem. The propellant required for topping of the tanks
during an 8-hr. ground hold with troops aboard, was calculated
to be a moderate 9 per cent of liquid hydrogen, and an additional
1·6 per cent of liquid oxygen.

Perhaps the era of the brute-force approach to space flight, which began with Sputnik, on 4 October 1967, may find itself superseded within a few years by the age of the technically sophisticated re-usable booster.

In view of this possibility, it may not be too soon to determine its most desirable design features. A transport, which can operate in the manner described in this chapter, rocketing immense battle units to distant war zones at sub-orbital speeds, could have an enormous impact on military strategy. It could modernize traditional military tactics by eliminating the need for conventional sea power and amphibious landing operations. Army logistics problems would be facilitated by the instant delivery of military supplies and equipment to anywhere in the world.

Development of this Space Age deterrent logistic fleet is not a 'way out' idea. Such vehicles could be designed without depending on any major scientific breakthrough; merely by extending the technology developed for post-Saturn rockets, Ithacus could come to pass.

An Ithacus-type vehicle would not exist exclusively for the military missions defined in this chapter. Its transport potential must be examined within the proper context, as a possible extension of re-usable booster technology. One might reasonably argue that this further application for re-usable launch vehicles establishes an indisputable *need* for such a device. However, as recently stated by NASA's Dr George E. Mueller, 'no one needed an airplane, a computer, or a telephone *before they existed*'.

Future troops need not be trained astronauts to ride the 'lightning-quick' rocket ship. Like Pegasus passengers, they would be subjected to only moderate decelerations, and would not have to wear space suits in the pressurized compartments. During re-entry, the deceleration peak would be above $1.5\ g$ for only 3 min., and above $2.0\ g$ for only 1 min.

Conventional modes of debarkation for the troops could include rope ladders, loop hoists, or slide chutes. In addition, Buck Rogers-type rocket packs which have already been developed for self-propelled troop mobility, would provide speedy exit and deployment after landing (page 81). Ithacus, though still in the conceptual stage, will perhaps one day be translated to nuts, bolts, and high-test beryllium and titanium. It could very well evolve into the most revolutionary by-product of our enveloping technological revolution.

Manned military rockets which follow a ballistic trajectory beyond the atmosphere over sovereign nations would create many controversial issues necessitating legal interpretation. A United Nations declaration clearly has demilitarized space and has identified the void above the Earth's atmosphere as international domain, to be used on an equal basis for peaceful purposes by all mankind. However, the vital question of where the atmosphere ends, and where outer space begins, has not yet been fully resolved.

The territorial rights of each nation extend into the air above it, just as national boundaries include the adjacent oceans, out to 12 (and in some cases, 3) nautical miles from a country's shores. By international law, derived from the doctrine of freedom of the seas, any nation has the right to protect its national security by destroying military reconnaissance aircraft violating the sovereign air space above it. But what of military rockets which overfly nations within the void above the maximum ascent ceiling of today's aircraft? Will they too be treated as hostile targets?

The response to the question of where to establish the peaceful dividing line between air space and outer space is currently being pondered by the greatest of our international legal minds. Perhaps the implementation of a truly international space co-operation programme will depend to a great extent on future jurisprudence, for which there is currently no precedent to be found.

CHAPTER EIGHT

THE COMMERCIAL SPACE STATION

The fruits of orbital research should begin to point towards important commercial dividends by 1980. By that time full analyses will have been made of a wide variety of experiments conducted by unmanned and manned space laboratories which could have direct benefit for the Earth community in such vital areas as agricultural prediction and control, forest resources inventory and protection, weather forecasting, air pollution and monitoring, cartography, water resources prediction, and aids to the fishing industry and commercial shipping. There will be new insight into the global distribution of minerals, oil, and fresh water. It should also be possible to begin, on a limited scale, industrial research into new materials and methods of fabrication exploiting the zero-g environment.

Looking towards this exciting future McDonnell-Douglas engineers have made a detailed study of a commercial space station which they suggest could have a permanent staff of 20 men. As well as providing service-type functions under government sponsorship, they envisage the space station of the 1980s as having separate modules equipped by industrial concerns. Launched separately they would rendezvous and dock with the 'government' station and receive support from it, allowing specially trained industrial scientists to concentrate on their own particular research assignments.

What would be acceptable economics for a co-operative government/commercial space station? To achieve realistic estimates, supply operations (amounting to approximately half of the operating costs) must be kept to a minimum. Some relief would, of course, be afforded if re-usable launch systems were available. If however, extended tours of duty in orbit were necessary, then naturally more spacious accommodation must be provided in orbit.

In working out the costs much depends on the detail tasks to be performed and how these would be applied in a practical way by Earth-based technology. The space segment is only part of the operation. Great improvements must be made in data analyses, storage, and distribution. But this, in itself, would help to generate a revolution in data-handling for government, scientific, and industrial purposes on a global scale providing a foundation for computerized data banks of the future. From such data depositories eventually mankind will find all his informational needs relayed by artificial satellite into offices, laboratories, and factories.

The requirements of high-capacity data analysis and distribution in Earth resources survey must serve to hasten this process.

All housekeeping functions aboard the parent space station would be performed by government personnel. A station commander and two deputies would be required for 'round-the-clock' operations. An administrative assistant would keep the station's log, process requisitions for resupply and data transmission, and deal with commercial personnel aboard the station and its industrial laboratories. Medical staff would consist of a physician/surgeon, appropriately trained in space medicine, and a male nurse, who might be an intern specializing in space medicine.

The operations and maintenance crew would maintain the basic laboratory, its sub-systems and equipment, and assist industrial personnel in operating and maintaining equipment. The applications group, several of whom would be of the doctorate level, would be supported by cross-training of communications personnel in such fields as geology, meteorology, agriculture, oceanography, and hydrology. Six members of the group would be civilian employees of the Weather Bureau, Department of Agriculture, Department of Commerce, and so forth, while the remainder would be commercial or public utility personnel recruited from the oil, shipping, fishing, and water resources industries.

Finally, the industrial personnel would comprise research teams of no more than three men each who would live in the basic space station but work in the individual research laboratories; they would be supported by the base station command, communications, medical, operations, and maintenance groups who would be government employees from international space consortia. The industrial research crews might represent such companies as DuPont, Johnson and Johnson, Starkist Tuna, United States Steel, Shell Oil, Union Carbide, and McDonnell-Douglas.

The space station (page 84) designed on the modular principle assumes the use of vehicles and structures developed for the lunar landing programme of the previous decade. This fixed the length and diameter of the station at 130 ft (39·6 m.) and 33 ft (10·06 m.) respectively. Total structural weight worked out at approximately 85,000 lb (38,500 kg.), with equipment and expendables adding another 150,000 to 200,000 lb (68,040 to 90,720 kg.).

As far as possible all basic functions to be performed are divided between different compartments or modules (page 83). Crew quarters are appointed three and a half modules. These include a command centre, wardroom for recreation and eating, wash and toilet facilities, a gymnasium, and a sick bay. Each crew-member has private quarters providing 7 × 7 ft (2·3 × 2·3 m.) of floor area sufficient for a bed and personal items.

The distribution of other station equipment can be seen in the diagram. Astronaut-conditioning equipment – including a centrifuge – is located between the crew quarters and the command station. Approximately 3,000 ft^2 (278·7 m.^{2}) of floor space is devoted to crew quarters and recreation.

Docking ports allowing for the transfer of personnel between the space station and supply craft from Earth are located in fore and aft modules together with housekeeping systems, stores, and EVA equipment which includes spacesuits and backpack propulsion units. In an adjacent module are cryogenics for the environmental and life-support systems, food storage, spare parts of various kinds, tools, and other maintenance equipment. The last two components and the nose cone contain the communications centre, Earth observation sensors, and associated services. Astronauts reach the various modules through a central tunnel.

This particular space-station concept allows a maximum of four industrial research and development laboratories, complete with equipment, to dock with the station for independent experiments. These are the paying customers. Their crews will be specially trained industrial personnel, and they will bring with them the bulk of their food, equipment, and spares. However, they will use crew quarters in the main station and draw on its power supplies and environmental services.

A typical industrial laboratory module, illustrated on page 84, would be docked with the station in conjunction with a supply craft. Weighing about 30,000 lb (13,608 kg.), it is approximately 30 ft (9·14 m.) long by 20 ft (6·09 m.) diameter and contains experimental equipment and expendables sufficient for six months.

When the mission is completed industrial personnel return to Earth in the supply craft and the laboratory can be either retained for further use or de-orbited for destruction over a remote area.

In defining a space station of this type power demands are a vital factor. As the 50 kW. requirements exceed the capability of a radioisotope system, and solar cells would become unwieldy, the Douglas designers anticipate the need for a reactor power system. In order to limit the need for shielding in the station this is installed in a pod on the end of a 100 ft (30·5 m.) boom. A base shield protects the station from harmful radiation and also minimizes its effects in the environment where the docking of supply craft occurs. Total weight of the reactor power system is approximately 25,000 lb (11,340 kg.) This includes a reactor with uranium-zirconium hydride fuel elements and a nominal 700-thermal-kW. capability, the necessary shielding, a Rankine or possibly Brayton-cycle power conversion system, and a radiator to dissipate waste heat.

Electrical power helps to run the environment control system for the station complex. An open oxygen cycle depends on the periodic supply of water to obtain breathing oxygen by electrolysis. Gaseous hydrogen released in this process, plus waste carbon dioxide and water from the crew, provide most of the propellant required for orbit-keeping by the resistojet propulsion system. The resistojet is so named because it uses electric resistance to heat liquid propellant, which is expanded through a jet nozzle for thrust. The thrust of the resistojet, measured in micropounds (millionths of a pound), can be applied over extremely long periods.

To cater for the large amounts of data storage in the parent station and each of the laboratory modules, Douglas proposed the use of photographic techniques using advanced laser technology.

This offers the prospect of data storage compression of the order of 10^2 or 10^3 over that of conventional magnetic tape systems. Although the crew would assess in real time as much data as possible, depending on the type of observation or experiment, a significant part of these data will be transmitted to the ground base using command facilities offered by the commercial network of Intelsat.

Operating costs of the overall space station are indicated below:

Debits	$ millions p.a.
Station	10
Operational spares	2
Logistics	101
Mission control	54
Crew training	20
Programme management	4·9
Salaries	1·2
	193·1
Assets	
Support rental fees	24
	169·1

Station costs include manufacture, equipment integration, and testing. Logistics costs assume a six-month duty cycle for the crew and a 50,000 lb (22,680 kg.) requirement for space station supply. This assumes a 9-man logistics vehicle with a cargo capacity of 25,000 lb (11,340 kg.) making two re-entry flights per year. Additional flights required for the total rotation of the 20-man permanent crew are satisfied by the launch of the industrial laboratories and re-entry of the 9-man crew modules.

The total annual operating cost to the government of $193·1 is reduced by rental fees from the industrial research and development laboratories which are estimated at about $6 million per industrial laboratory. Annual costs for the laboratory modules, additional to primary station operating costs, are as follows:

		$ millions p.a.
Laboratory cost		10
Laboratory purchase	5·0	
Laboratory equipment	5·0	
Laboratory launch (including logistic vehicle)		50
Operating costs		21·2
Laboratory costs	2·0	
Mission control	7·0	
Crew training	6·0	
Crew salaries	0·18	
Support rental fee	6·0	
		81·2

The economic value of a station complex of this kind depends on the operational benefits, and specifically upon tasks which can be accomplished uniquely or more effectively in space than in any other way. While any single application is unlikely to provide economic justification for a space project of this magnitude, total benefits affecting the many applications reviewed in Chapter One, show every prospect of justifying manned space-station development.

The McDonnell-Douglas team responsible for the study on commercial space stations examined 11 major areas of Earth application from which the anticipated economic benefits are listed below:

An *agricultural census* including advanced detection of crop diseases has been estimated at between $10 to $100 million p.a. Orbital monitoring, it is suggested, could reduce substantially the present annual cost of $40 million expended by the US Department of Agriculture in checking contract compliance by farmers in the United States. Natural disasters due to earthquakes, floods, drought, famine, and destructive storms (hurricanes, typhoons, etc.) could be rapidly assessed, giving accurate forecasts of relief expenditures.

Advantages are also claimed for *cartography* in providing unique opportunities for the preparation and revision of maps of all kinds affecting the world land mass. The annual savings for updating alone could amount to some $10 million.

Forestry is another important area. Estimates suggest that a forest inventory made from space would represent a cost saving of 40 per cent over conventional methods. The ability of the space station to detect forest fires might result in 8 per cent reduction of the total forest area burned, and a net saving of $32 million. Allied to the *fishing industry* continuous space observation of the continental shelves, estuaries, and oceans, could provide data on fish migration, determine a relationship between the sea environment and fish supply, and provide a means of locating fishing-grounds. It has been estimated that the National Oceanography Programme will increase the US fish harvest by about $600 million. Fisheries observation from a space station might increase this by $50 million.

Geographic studies from space affect the optimum use of land, transportation, and population growth and distribution.

Hydrology looks at the Earth's water resources. Douglas engineers summarize the position as follows:

> The US Department of Commerce estimates that the water usage in the United States will increase from the present 370 to 500 billion gallons per day by 1980. At present this represents an investment of $40 million per year. It is estimated that one-half or $20 million per year in the United States and, by 1980, $100 million world-wide, can be saved by use of a space station determining such information as snow and ice cover, vegetative cover, land use, and river basin geomorphology. In addition, such data will aid in locating unused water sources in the underdeveloped or remote regions, as well as aiding in more accurate predictions of known sources. For example, a single medium-sized Canadian hydroelectric plant can save $1 million for each 1 per cent increase in accuracy by predicting April-to-August flow.

Using remote sensing techniques to locate possible new areas of *mineral deposits* might result in $10 million-a-year additional yield.

Oceanography is another fertile area. Integration of space-sensing techniques with new efforts to probe the oceans may achieve large economies. Savings of some $10 million a year are predicted, taking into account the opportunities for marine mineral resources and coastal development.

Probing the Earth for new oilfields may be perfected with the use of orbital observation. It is estimated that the US yield of oil will increase by $8,000 to $9,000 million per year by 1980. Of this $50 million per year could be attributed to orbital detection.

Finding the best routes for ships can also have economic value. The operating costs of ocean-going vessels range from $1,000 to $10,000 per day and the mapping of ocean currents and forecasting of ocean waves can be important to the economic routeing of ships. An example is the wave-forecasting system developed by the Naval Oceanographic Office and used by the Military Sea Transport Service. This is estimated to have saved about 18 to 20 hr. per average crossing in all weathers. These savings are all the more impressive when it is realized that 180,000 ocean crossings per year are anticipated by 1980 and that the average operating cost of ocean-going vessels is $3,000 per day. Many factors will operate in holding down costs in the future, including unmanned weather satellites, advances in communications, decreased ship operating costs, improved ship design, and an international buoy-forecasting system. The manned orbital laboratory will expand the opportunities for space sensing and high-speed communication of sea-state data.

The economic importance of accurate long-range weather prediction in many areas of human activity cannot be emphasized too strongly. A report by the National Research Council of the US National Academy of Science estimates total savings could exceed $2,000 million a year. They could arise from natural resources, agriculture, transportation, trade, disaster warnings, and fishing, to name a few. The estimates do not take into account economic benefits that might be obtained in industries connected with tourism and recreation, or the savings to individual families. The breakdown of savings is as follows: flood and storm damage $70–140 million; new construction $1,000 million; fuels and electric power $500 million; fruit and vegetable production $500 million; and livestock production $450 million.

A study made by the Stanford Research Institute put the annual value of long-term weather forecasts of monsoons in south-east

Asia at $700 million. It was also pointed out that average hurricane costs for the North American continent were about $309 million, including damage, protection, and surveillance. One investigator believes an orbital warning system could save North America about $25 million during an average season, while the value of a two-week forecast to the agricultural industry has been variously estimated at anything between $4,300 and $11,000 million. The only chance of getting near this order of weather prediction rests with refinement of space technique.

McDonnell-Douglas put the total world economic benefit of the 1980 Commercial Space Station at $6,700 million. The total net commercial return for comparison with space-station operating costs is indicated in the last column of the table. This does not include capital preservation or orbital applications benefits, such as weather forecasting, that would ordinarily be provided as a government service. Of the total $262 million, $147 million can be related to commercial enterprises or public utilities, while $115 million represents government savings. This is considered an extremely conservative estimate in the light of a Communications Satellite Corporation prediction that the corporative earnings would almost triple between 1966 and 1968, and that a hundredfold revenue increase is possible in the next five years.

What else may be expected from space-station technology? In a keynote speech before the British Interplanetary Society in London, Dr George E. Mueller, NASA's Associate Administrator, Manned Space Flight, forecast the development of factory processes unique to the space environment. He pointed out that under zero-gravity conditions in orbit, molecular forces – which have little or no role in Earth-based manufacture – could become controlling factors in new manufacturing techniques. Surface tension and capillary forces, for instance, can be made to dominate processes in the zero-g environment.

Again, buoyancy effects disappear and components of different density in a mixture do not demix; mixing by convection currents does not occur. A neutral condition replaces directional stability and instability. Stability exists, however, in that liquid is not drained out between surface tension layers as happens on Earth. Therefore, it seems that stable foam can be produced from any liquid and gas mixture in zero gravity. Examples of zero-gravity manufacturing processes 'are now absorbing the attention of some of our scientists and engineers', Dr Mueller told the Society. They include free-fall casting and blowing, zero-*g* foaming and zero-*g* surface tension coating.

Material in the liquid state floating in a mere zero-*g* environment will finally take the form of a perfect sphere. Thus it is conceivable that metal ball-bearings can be manufactured in space to tolerances of plus or minus Angström units, impossible in our present technology. Ball-bearings made to these tolerances could revolutionize our machine-based civilization, Dr Mueller said, by reducing friction and noise levels to the vanishing point, providing new levels of precision.

The requirements now exists for precision hollow-sphere ball-bearings to move large radar antennae, rotate large aircraft wings, and support loads in jet-engines.

By injecting gas into the centre of molten-metal perfect spheres, precision hollow spheres, can be formed which are at present impossible to produce in one piece. Spinning, free-floating spheres during the chilling phase can produce accurate ellipsoidal shapes to tolerances absolutely impossible to produce on Earth. The application of electrostatic fields could be used to distort the molten metal into many different shapes for many different design purposes to precision tolerances that are impossible to obtain with terrestrial technology.

Free-fall casting techniques could also be utilized to cast large optical blanks for telescopes which would be completely free of flaws and distortion.

Stable foams for a wide variety of liquefied materials and gases offer exciting possibilities. Under terrestrial conditions, such foams cannot be produced in an equilibrium condition because of the demixing buoyancy action and draining of the subsurface liquid caused by gravity. Under zero gravity, the mixing and equal distribution of gas bubbles in any liquid can be stabilized, and further application of field forces by linear or centrifugal acceleration or electrostatic fields can move the bubble distribution into a desired pattern. Gas-bubble size can be controlled by mixing techniques and adjustment of gas pressure. Thus novel combined materials like steel and glass of drastically different densities and properties could be produced. Structures with a new optimum strength-to-weight ratio, temperature compatibility, and ductility, could be developed. Drastic improvements in the brittle behaviour of materials might also be achieved because the micropore structure would act as crack stoppers.

Potential applications of micropore foam materials are extremely light-weight armour-plates, variable-density turbine blades, and insulation materials to compensate for varying high-temperature gradients.

If we are eventually to see the space environment exploited in this way large space stations will be required catering for more people and an expanded range of laboratory and production facilities.

McDonnell-Douglas, looking beyond 1990, have included in their studies the concept of a 'second-generation', 400-man, commercial space station which capitalizes on a low-cost logistic system. This large station is of modular design, providing artificial or zero gravity for various functions which could include the vacuum deposition of materials, vacuum melting of alloys, vacuum welding, vacuum tube production, pharmacology, pharmacohorticulture, accelerated growth of genetic strains, and the development and manufacture of the products for further space ventures.

Examples of space vacuum technology cited in the survey include the refinement of silicon or germanium to the high degree of purity required for transistors and deposited circuitry, and appropriate alloying of this material to produce either P- or N-type semi-conductors; also the deposition of microelectric circuitry. As the material quantities are relatively small and the end product relatively expensive, mass-production techniques in space might be competitive with industrial facilities on Earth. Other candidate products might be high-power vacuum tubes needed in the communications, X-ray, microwave, and laser fields. Production of such tubes depends on highly expensive and critical processes which are well adapted to electron-beam welding techniques and able to take full advantage of the hard vacuum available in orbit.

As more specialists in different fields of science and technology come to study the opportunities for orbital research, development, and production, the list of useful applications may be expected to grow, often in quite unexpected directions. Benefits to medical science should be no exception. For example, it is possible that the costly raw materials from which certain drugs are produced could be made, in some cases, without the need for high-cost synthesis. The opportunities stem from biological research with plants conducted in unmanned space-satellites. In a weightless environment, it is found that most of the energy supplied to the plant need not be imported to the stalk or trunk of a drug-producing bush or tree but into the leaves or flowers. It is estimated that in the Earth's $1 g$ field 85 per cent of the energy goes into the stalk. Under zero-gravity conditions exactly the reverse applies, which has led to the idea of high-yield, drug-producing plants being grown in space. Moreover, the sterile environment of orbital space could provide the ultraclean rooms now required in the packaging and processing of certain drugs.

It is also possible that the zero-g environment will assist in producing forms of genetic strains faster for use in the fields of agriculture, fermentation, and animal husbandry. Once such agricultural or animal strains have been developed in orbit, the subjects may be transported to Earth for subsequent propagation.

Researchers have also pointed out that since antibodies are produced through fermentation procedures, swifter and cheaper methods of antibiotic production may emerge from orbital technology.

As man embarks on new space ventures such as a lunar base and interplanetary exploration, space-manufacturing techniques will find further outlets. Spaceships will be assembled and serviced at space station 'cosmodromes', and structures and components required for further space achievement may be partly fabricated in orbit. Typical of new manufacturing techniques unique to the weightless environment, as already mentioned, are micropore foam structures which could be used for the construction of pressurized buildings on the Moon and Mars. Fundamental to the economics of the station would be the availability of low-cost, re-usable, launch systems to provide the necessary logistics support.

CHAPTER NINE

INTERPLANETARY EXPLORATION

Whether or not we shall be anticipating the first manned exploration of Mars in the 1980s, as we anticipated the first manned lunar landings in the 1960s, depends on a variety of unknowns. It is unlikely that any firm decision will be taken until laboratory capsules have been landed from unmanned probes to ascertain basic parameters. Evidence of biological development on the planet clearly would be a strong inducement to develop manned systems.

In the United States the Science Advisory Committee, having pressed strongly for unmanned exploration of Venus and Mars, has taken a cautious line in terms of manned interplanetary flight. They say it is premature to establish any fixed timetable or even to be certain which planet will be the priority objective. There is a need for specific identification of man's unique, or most effective, role in planetary exploration, and to achieve a proper co-ordination of manned and unmanned activities.

After the Moon, Mars and Venus received periodic visits from space probes serving as robot 'path-finders'. An instrument capsule ejected for soft-landing from the Soviet spacecraft Venus 4 in October 1967 confirmed exceedingly high temperatures beneath the thick atmospheric blanket, and maximum interest in the 1970s centres on Mars, the so-called 'Red Planet'.

On Mars new and exciting opportunities are opening, for it may not be long before space probes turn up the first evidence that life has evolved independently on another planet. Even the discovery of bacteria would be starting confirmation of life's versatility. For if living cells have emerged on a neighbouring planet, under such rigorous conditions, the chances of similar developments elsewhere in the Universe must be extremely high. Here the interests of space research and medical science may merge to the benefit of mankind, for a greater understanding of the living cell is fundamental to winning the battle against malignant disease. It is not without significance that important experiments concerning the structure of living matter are now taking place in research centres devoted to advanced space problems.

For a long time astronomers have spoken of blue-green areas covering about one-third of the Martian surface which gradually change in outline and colour. This led to a theory that primitive vegetation, peculiar to the Martian environment, had sprung up on Mars and that the colour changes followed a seasonal cycle suggestive of growth and decay. The celebrated 'canals' have been related to this phenomenon. But when America's Mariner 4 spacecraft came within 8,000 miles (12,875 km.) of Mars in July 1965, its photographs told a different story. The 21 pictures it transmitted to Earth revealed that at least part of the surface is covered by hundreds of moon-like craters. However, the Mariner camera scanned less than 1 per cent of the surface; and the spacecraft was too far away to resolve small surface detail. What certain pictures did appear to show, however, was a form of hoarfrost or carbon dioxide snow fringing some of the craters 10 to 15° from the south polar cap.

Supporting the camera survey were other significant results. The helium vector magnetometer did not record any appreciable magnetic field, nor did the three Geiger-Mueller tubes and solid-state detector find any evidence of magnetically trapped radiation in the neighbourhood of Mars equivalent to the Earth's Van Allen radiation belt. This may indicate that Mars has a solid core.

The Martian atmosphere was also investigated by an indirect method. During the period of the probe's occultation by the planet, its radio signals passed directly through the Martian atmosphere. By observing changes in the frequency, phase, and amplitude, it was possible to deduce that the surface atmospheric pressure is about 9 millibars (equivalent to conditions some 20 miles (32·2 km.) above the Earth's surface). This was rather less than had been estimated from purely Earth observation. From analyses of the absorption spectrum of light scattered from the planet, it appears that the thin Martian atmosphere contains carbon dioxide. Other constituents are believed to be nitrogen with traces of rare gases such as argon. The surface pressure is, of course, far too low for astronauts to exist with purely breathing apparatus; a full pressure suit is essential.

The effective atmosphere extending from 5 to 6·2 miles (8 to 10 km.), though allowing some aerodynamic braking, will be insufficient for spacecraft to land using parachutes alone. It is therefore necessary to employ retro-rocket systems similar to those developed for Surveyor and the Apollo lunar module for terminal manœuvres and soft-landing.

In assessing the prospects for a manned flyby mission to Mars, the Science Advisory Committee argues that this 'does not appear to utilize man in a unique role'; also, one must recognize the great uncertainty necessarily associated with schedule and cost estimates 'in the absence of any experience relevant to the reliability of equipment and the capabilities of men on interplanetary missions of durations fifty times longer than the Apollo mission'.

Once again this emphasizes the need to consolidate experience in Earth orbit in the Apollo Applications Programme. Many of the basic parameters of manned interplanetary flight can be simulated in rudimentary space stations developed from Apollo hardware, including bio-medical experience of several months' duration.

Only after such experience has been obtained will it be possible to take the first steps in human exploration of the nearer planets which, initially, may call for a mix of manned and unmanned systems. The Committee comments:

> One can envision a manned Mars – or Venus – orbiter in which the crew orbits around the planet but does not land, while controlling from orbit a number of unmanned probes and soft-landed mobile vehicles in real time. One of the unmanned probes might scoop up a small sample of Martian soil, encapsulate the sample, and then launch the capsule towards a rendezvous with the mother craft in orbit. Although in principle many of these functions could be carried out by means of a fully automated, preprogrammed system, the complexity of such a system and the need for redundancy (duplicate systems) might be so great that the crew may more than pay its own way.
>
> Compared to a direct manned landing, a manned orbiting expedition has the great advantage of requiring a

substantially lower initial (vehicle) mass in Earth-orbit. In addition, it permits us to concentrate on solving the sterilization problems with unmanned subsystems before attempting the more difficult problem of manned landing.

In view of these problems it is difficult to see manned flights to the planets before the mid-1980s. The Committee's view is that any earlier commitment would mean reliance on Apollo technology, much of which 'was necessarily frozen into 1961–63 state-of-the-art'. By adopting a more leisurely schedule for manned planetary flight, time might be bought 'for a vigorous development of new and more efficient on-board power supply and other critical subsystems, thus permitting an orderly increase in total space capability. Most importantly, we would then have the necessary time to design man into the system than to have him primarily as a passenger.'

It would also allow time for a proper evaluation to be made between various propulsive techniques – chemical, nuclear, and nuclear-electric; also to establish techniques for assembly and fuelling vehicles in Earth orbit.

What is the Soviet attitude to interplanetary exploration? To judge from the bold pronouncements of scientists and others connected with the space programme, man is the cardinal instrument, the space probe merely a path-finder.

Academician Anatoly Blagonravov, chairman of the Committee for the Exploration and Use of Outer Space, USSR Academy of Sciences, puts the position quite plainly:

> However great the possibilities of modern automatic and cybernetic devices may be, they are still very far from man's varied and primarily creative possibilities. Even the most 'ingenious' present-day automatic devices can act either according to a given programme, or at best improve this programme during the course of operation. But in compiling a programme for cybernetic machines, including self-learning ones, it is necessary to have certain initial data about the phenomenon studied.
>
> Yet as we penetrate deeper into space, we shall more often encounter phenomenon about which we knew nothing at all

in advance. Quite often we shall be challenged by problems which do not seem to be capable of formulation in advance. This, however, is practically the most essential aspect of the study of outer space. It is the challenge of entirely new and unpredicted problems that, in the final analysis, ensures those qualitative leaps that substantially increase our knowledge.

One should also not forget the subconcious activity of the human brain, Blagonravov says,

about intuition which is so far beyond the potentialities of the cybernetic machine. Yet it is a fact that the subconscious and intuition play an extremely large role in the process of the scientific investigation of nature. . . . Since at the present stage of space exploration one of the key tasks consists in gaining ever more profound knowledge of nature, man's direct participation in spaceflight is absolutely necessary.

Man's direct involvement in a largely automatically controlled space vehicle has been a consistent argument throughout the entire history of Soviet space development and one is struck by the close relationship with principles established by the Father of Soviet Cosmonautics, Konstantin E. Tsiolkovsky. Although proper attention has been paid to unmanned satellites and space probes to establish basic parameters, there can be little doubt that central to Soviet ambitions is a desire to achieve an integration between the unique qualities of man, on the one hand, and the cybernetic machine on the other.

How is the immense task of exploring the planets to be undertaken? In view of the enormous cost and complexity of this type of exploration, there would be logic in Russia and America planning joint expeditions, building up stores and equipment first in Earth orbit and then making group flights into orbit at the destination planet. Whether or not this type of combined operation can be managed politically remains to be seen.

Meanwhile, the technical requirements of missions to the nearer planets already have been studied in considerable depth by aerospace engineers. 'A Conceptual design for a Manned Mars Vehicle' was the title of a technical paper presented by one of the

authors at the Stockholm Congress of the International Astronautical Federation (IAF) in 1960. This concluded that it was
indeed possible to accomplish a manned landing on Mars with a
chemically propelled rocket, using liquid oxygen and liquid
hydrogen propellants. However, in order to keep the vehicle's
initial mass within practical limits, this parallel (side-by-side)
staged concept, using plug-nozzle engines, necessitated an
excessive two years and nine months for the round trip from Earth
to Mars, clearly an unreasonably long mission duration. To minimize energy requirements, the vehicle followed the well-known
Hohmann semi-elliptical paths between the two planetary orbits,
requiring 259 days to travel each leg of the journey. Unavoidably,
such trajectories make it necessary to wait on Mars for 479 days
before the two planets are again suitably positioned in their
respective orbits for the minimum-energy (but maximum-
duration) return voyage to begin.

Unquestionably, nuclear propulsion will be required in order
to reduce both the vehicle mass and the transmit time to more
realistic proportions. A six- to eight-man crew, a 450-day round
trip time, and an Earth-launch target date of early April 1986
are possible objectives. Significantly, a perihelion opposition will
occur in 1986, bringing Mars as close to Earth as it ever approaches
our planet. Due to the eccentricity of Mars' orbit, such a favourable
low-energy opportunity would not occur again until 15 years
later; in the year 2001. Excessive mission energy requirements, of
course, would be reflected in the required size for the interplanetary
spacecraft.

In 1963, an extensive conceptual study was implemented on
chemo-nuclear launch vehicles which could perform a mission to
land men on Mars in 1986. A ROMBUS-type (see Chapter Five)
of launch vehicle was employed in the study to boost the nuclear-
powered spacecraft to a 100,000 ft (30,500 m.) altitude, then
separate and return to Earth. Once above the major portion of the
atmosphere, the nuclear engines could be safely ignited without
atmospheric reflection of radiation upon the crew, or without
radioactive exhaust products falling back to Earth. After boosting
the spacecraft into the initial 'parking' orbit, the nuclear engines
would be reignited for departure. It was determined that a mass of

2 million lb (908,000 kg.) would be required in Earth orbit for this nuclear spaceship to perform a 450-day round trip. Of this transit time, the outbound journey to Mars could be performed in 170 days; five crew members would use an electrically powered surface vehicle to explore the planet for 30 days, and the return trip to Earth would then take an additional 250 days. Reduction of outbound trip time from 259 to 170 days would necessitate imparting much more kinetic energy to the spacecraft upon departure from Earth. This would have to be nullified upon arrival at Mars, resulting in further increased vehicle mass. The return trip – like the conceptual design presented at the IAF – would consist of a quasi-minimum-energy transfer.

Quite unexpectedly, the 1·5 million lb (681,000 kg.) of nuclear thrust required at an altitude of 100,000 ft (30,500 m.) for sub-orbital boost during this mode of operation, led to some profound technological soul-searching. The nuclear reactor necessary to heat sufficient hydrogen expellant to produce a thrust of this magnitude would be so large and so complex, that its availability for the mission target date became highly questionable. However, the required thrust level can be reduced by starting the nuclear engines in orbit, since the thrust then need be only 30 per cent of the vehicle weight. Five propulsion modules (requiring a total of six months to assemble in Earth orbit) would each incorporate a single NERVA 2 nuclear engine producing 200,000 lb (90,800 kg.) of thrust. Unfortunately, one of the three stages – the Earth-escape stage – would be comprised of three such clustered 33 ft (10 m.) diameter modules, generating a total thrust of 600,000 lb (272,400 kg.). At that point in time, it did not appear that NERVA reactors (available in the late 1970s) could be effectively clustered for producing the cumulative thrust level. It was believed that leaking neutrons from one reactor would cross-couple it to an adjacent reactor, adversely affecting the controllability, internal flow stability, and performance. This problem of nucleonic inter-action from incident neutrons between closely clustered reactors is no longer considered to be of unmanageable proportions, even with a minimum of shielding. . . . .

By comparison, it was determined that, with all-chemical pro-pulsion, twice as much initial weight would be required in Earth orbit at the outset of the mission, or approximately 4 million lb (1·82 million kg.). For that study, it was assumed that ROMBUS-type vehicles would also be required to boost the specially developed chemically propelled spacecraft modules to Earth orbit for assembly. At this point, it became evident that both types of Mars spacecraft – either the nuclear or the chemically propelled variety – depended on a ROMBUS-sized launch vehicle. This raised an important question. Was it possible to reduce the enormous development costs associated with either variety of Mars space-craft? Could the entire mission be performed by a specially modi-fied derivative of the ROMBUS vehicle? Clearly, such an approach would not produce an optimized-weight design, but it might result in *minimum programme cost* and minimum development time.

With the minimum-cost objective in mind, ROMBUS was adapted for Project Deimos, named after one of the moons of Mars. Artists' impressions of this proposed application appear on pages 88–91. A 76,000 lb (34,400 kg.) toroidal crew compartment was installed above the spherical liquid oxygen tank located in the ROMBUS centre-body. Approximately 14,000 lb (6,360 kg.) of sustenance items were included to accommodate the crew for the entire trip. A 55,000 lb (25,000 kg.) Mars landing module was incorporated at the top of the combined command-centre living-quarters. A collapsible transportation vehicle and inflatable crew quarters, for use on Mars' surface, were included in the payload.

In Project Deimos, four external hydrogen tanks would be jettisoned upon reaching Earth escape velocity, a diametrically opposed pair would be discarded after retro-thrust into Mars orbit, and the remaining two fuel tanks would be 'staged' after escaping from Mars. The Mars landing module would contain its own on-board propellants for soft-landing on the planet, and for Mars launch. The manned capsule would then rendezvous with the Earth-return spacecraft which had been 'parked' in Mars orbit.

The Project Deimos study concluded that a huge 14 million lb (6·36 million kg.) payload would be required in Earth orbit at the start of the mission, 3·5 times as much as the weight-optimized and specially designed chemically propelled spacecraft. This increased required weight, consisting mainly of propellants, was a result of the inefficient operational technique employed, boosting the weight of the entire ROMBUS vehicle on a round trip between the heliocentric orbits of Earth and Mars. Thus, although this operational mode resulted in far-from-optimum equivalent weights in Earth orbit, the study identified some dramatic cost reductions. These economies would be consistent with widespread adaptation of re-usable launch vehicles for multi-purpose missions in Earth-orbital and lunar operations.

The very reasons which rendered this operational technique unattractive from a weights standpoint made this particular approach desirable from a low-cost point of view. Through orbital refuelling, the same basic chemically propelled launch vehicle could replace the entire Mars spacecraft, then serving as a multi-functional unit. (Illustrations on pages 86–87 show this technique also applied in a lunar mission (Project Selena) with ROMBUS). The launch vehicle also could be used for the Earth-escape stage, the propulsion stage for establishing a Mars orbit, the Mars-escape stage, and the Earth-re-entry module. In addition, this scheme would enhance the probability of mission success. By employing a multi-purpose vehicle which had been improved and perfected through repeated re-use – rather than a relatively unproven newly developed expendable spacecraft – significant reliability gains would unquestionably accrue.

The initial launch for Project Deimos would consist of the ROMBUS vehicle modified to accept the toroidal crew compartment, protected during ascent by a jettisonable nose fairing. This vehicle would deplete its propellants, and drop its external tanks, while acquiring orbital velocity. A fleet of re-usable ROMBUS-type tankers, each carrying 400 tons (362,800 kg.) of fully loaded hydrogen tanks as its payload, would refuel the initial spacecraft in orbit. In certain cases, the orbital tanker versions would pump liquid oxygen from their payload compartment to the internal spherical tank of the planetary vehicle. These techniques avoid the need for pumping low-density hydrogen in orbit. The full liquid hydrogen tanks could be readily coupled to the spacecraft centre-body. By restricting the orbital operations to refuelling only, which could be accomplished in one month or less, the otherwise complex (and expensive) orbital assembly techniques (as discussed for the minimum-weight spacecraft) could be completely circumvented.

A nuclear propulsion system cannot be used during launch from Earth, as previously noted, because of the danger of radioactive exhaust products falling upon populated areas. Nor can such an engine be operated within the Earth's atmosphere if there are men aboard the vehicle, unless the cabin is completely shielded against scattered radiation from all directions. The primary application for this high-performance propulsive device would be to impart the necessary velocity for accelerating the manned vehicle from Earth orbit to escape velocity, and to inject it into the interplanetary trajectory. Thus, it appears certain that a high-thrust system – either chemical or nuclear propulsion – is mandatory for departure from Earth orbit.

An electric propulsion system would probably be used for unmanned vehicles, or for extremely high-energy manned missions to the outer planets. On such missions, the ion or plasma motor would then be started in deep space, after escaping Earth. It does not appear practicable to start this high-performance (but low-thrust) propulsion device in Earth orbit, during a manned mission to Mars, for example. Because of its low thrust, the electrically propelled manned vehicle would need to follow a spiral accelera-tion path around Earth while accumulating velocity in order to escape our planet's gravitational field. During this long interval, the crew would be exposed to radiation from the Van Allen belts. The inner belt begins at about 300 miles (483 km.) above the Earth's surface, but its most dangerously radioactive portion extends from 1,200 miles (1,930 km.) to 1,400 miles (2,250 km.) above Earth. The core of the less-hazardous outer-Van Allen belt extends from 10,000 miles (16,100 km.) to 15,000 miles (24,100 km.) above Earth.

Conceivably, the crew could be subjected to the maximum allowable radiation dosage during any long stay within the Van Allen belts. Further prohibitive radiation which might be en-countered during the remainder of the mission – as from solar flares – could exceed the allowable physiological dosage. Typically, if a 250,000 lb (113,400 kg.) thrust nuclear (or chemical) pro-pulsion system could accelerate the manned vehicle from orbital velocity to escape velocity in five minutes, a 20 lb (9·07 kg.) thrust electric system would have to operate 12,500 times longer – or for 43·4 days – in order to impart the same velocity increment to the spacecraft. Psychologically, the crew would not accept the wasteful expenditure of almost a month and a half, before even beginning their transplanetary voyage – nor could man physiologically tolerate extended exposure to radiation from the Van Allen belts, for even a matter of weeks.

Nevertheless, 14 million lb (6·36 million kg.) – or indeed, even 4 million lb (1·82 million kg.) in Earth orbit – constitute a required mass of staggering proportions. Nuclear propulsion, with its associated increased specific impulse, can reduce these initial weights to a wieldable size, while still performing the manned round trip to Mars within 450 days or less. Moreover, the initially required weight (in Earth orbit) for nuclear spacecraft is far less sensitive to variations in launch opportunities. For example, such a mission using nuclear energy could be launched in cycles of two years two months, during the less-favourable years of 1979 to 1984, without increasing the required mass of 2 million lb (908,000 kg.) by more than 500,000 lb (227,000 kg.) for any particular launch window. By comparison, the 4 million lb (1·82 million kg.) required for a 1986 launch with an all-chemical weight-optimized system would have to be doubled, in the event that a 1979 launch were required. In the interests of consistency, all-chemical or nuclear vehicles investigated during the study assumed aerodynamic braking at Mars and upon return to Earth.

Research and development on nuclear propulsion has been in progress for many years in the United States and there are suspicions that the Soviet space programme also includes work on nuclear rockets. This impression is based on more than vague hints from Soviet scientists. When asked by Senator Cannon during House Committee hearings if he had any indication of Soviet work on nuclear rocket engines, Mr James E. Webb, the former NASA Administrator, said: 'The answer has to be yes, Senator, but not of the kind that I can discuss in an open meeting.'

How soon Soviet nuclear rockets will appear remains to be seen. Equivalent work in the United States began at Los Alamos in 1955 and has progressed through several experimental stages, test-bed reactors having run on both gaseous and liquid hydrogen at the Nevada Test Site.

The principle of the nuclear rocket is basically simple. Instead of using the heat of conventional chemical combustion, the atomic rocket depends on forcing a propellant of low molecular weight, such as liquid hydrogen, through a high-temperature reactor. The reactor flashes the hydrogen into a powerful propelling jet which exhausts from a convergent-divergent nozzle (pages 92–93).

Developing a practical system, however, involves huge problems. Liquid hydrogen, stored at a temperature approaching absolute zero ($-248°$ C) ($-478°$ F), must be pumped to the reactor and instantly raised to a temperature above $2,200°$ C ($3,992°$ F). The reactor must be sufficiently reliable to run for long periods – 30 to 45 min. for a mission to Mars – and radiation problems must be dealt with by suitable shielding.

The nuclear rocket's big advantage is its much higher exhaust velocity which can be twice that of the best chemical rockets. In engineering terms this means a higher specific impulse which is defined as pounds (or kilogrammes) of thrust per pound (or kilogramme) of propellant flow per second. The high specific impulse available reduces the total amount of propellant required for a given mission but, because of the low density of the fluid, larger storage tanks are required. Nuclear engines will also be heavier than conventional liquid-propellant rocket engines and, on a simple comparison of thrust, will be considerably more expensive to produce.

Thrust, however, is not the important parameter. Because of the doubled exhaust velocity, the nuclear rocket uses only half as much propellant each second of engine operation so that, in terms of performance, it can achieve far more than a chemical rocket of equal thrust. For the more ambitious missions, such as hauling heavy payloads between Earth and Moon, or sending expeditions to the planets, it has distinct advantages. In fact, the higher propulsive efficiencies may be expected to pay off by *reducing* overall mission costs.

At the Madrid International Astronomical Federation Congress in 1966, Mr Harold B. Finger of the Space Nuclear Propulsion Office of AEC and NASA, gave an encouraging progress report.

He revealed that the programme had experimentally demonstrated altitude specific impulses better than 760 lb-sec./lb assuming a nozzle area ratio of 40 to 1. An operating time of 30 min. had been achieved at this specific impulse at the full design power of 1,100 MW.

The experimental reactors KIWI and NERVA had graphite fuel elements through which the hydrogen is passed to form the propulsive jet. The fissionable material in these fuel elements was in the form of pyrolytic-carbon-coated particles of uranium carbide. Flow passages in the fuel elements were coated with niobium carbide to protect the graphite from the corrosive effect of the hydrogen.

The latest experimental reactor in 1966, described as a 'breadboard engine', had the turbo-pump mounted directly on the railway flatwagon on which it was test-fired in an inverted position adjacent to the test stand. The wagon allowed the reactor to be withdrawn in safety by means of a remote-controlled locomotive after the test was finished.

The encouraging results of this work led to the decision to proceed with a flight-rated NERVA 1 engine with a thrust of some 75,000 lb (34,019 kg.). Although this is far from the optimum size required for manned interplanetary exploration, the thrust level is sufficient for less demanding missions and, at the same time, gives vital experience for the development of larger nuclear engines.

NERVA 1 would be particularly effective as a replacement for the existing S-IVB stage of Saturn 5. The launcher's first two stages would serve to place the nuclear third stage into a close Earth orbit and the mission could proceed from there. Alternatively, the nuclear stage could be restarted before getting into orbit as in the case of the chemical S-IVB.

The higher specific impulse obtainable from the nuclear stage would have the effect of uprating the Saturn 5 by a factor of approximately two, increasing the payload for deep space missions by 80 to 100 per cent or alternatively shortening transit times. On flights to the Moon payloads would be increased by about 65 per cent.

In 1969 test firings in a vertical stand began of the NASA/AEC

NERVA-XE liquid hydrogen experimental nuclear rocket engine of 50,000 lb (22 680 kg) thrust at the Nuclear Rocket Development Station, Jackass Flats, Nevada. This was the non-flying prototype of the NERVA 1 engine of 75,000 lb (34 019 kg) thrust expected to be flight tested in the late 1970s.

The preferred engine for manned interplanetary flight is the larger NERVA 2, development of which has been frustrated by cuts in the space budget. The engine itself, 40 ft (12·2 m.) tall, would have a reactor of 6 ft (1·83 m.) external diameter with a nozzle area ratio of 80–100 to 1. Operating at 5,000 MW., it would deliver a thrust of 200,000 to 250,000 lb (90,720 to 113,400 kg.) for a minimum of 30 min. Based on reactor temperatures already achieved, a specific impulse of 825 lb-sec./lb should be readily attainable.

This, too, could be substituted for the existing third stage of Saturn 5, in the shape of a 33 ft (10·05 m.) diameter propulsion module. It would be applicable to direct lunar missions, such as the supply of a lunar base, for manned flyby missions to Mars and Venus and Mars lander excursions. For the lander mission, 1·5 to 2·5 million lb (0·68 to 1·15 million kg.) would have to be delivered into Earth orbit, involving orbital assembly and fuelling techniques. But if these had to depend on chemical rockets alone, the payload delivered into Earth orbit would have to be two to four times as great. The nuclear propulsion module, therefore, would economize on the number of Saturn 5 launchers.

For docking up to a spacecraft in orbit or joining up to another propulsion module (page 94), the nose of the nuclear module would be provided with appropriate probes and receptors for automatic coupling following the principle demonstrated by Gemini and its Agena target, or Cosmos and Soyuz docking vehicles.

In the case of a lunar mission estimates suggest that 75 per cent more payload could be landed as compared with the original Apollo system. A manned fly-by to Mars would need only 40 per cent of the payload delivered into orbit which a purely chemical rocket requires to fly this mission, while the saving for a Saturn fly-by would be 65 to 85 per cent.

The nuclear rocket as described is not the only way of applying atomic energy for space travel. Much is expected of nuclear-electric propulsion systems where very much higher specific impulses are attainable at low thrust values.

Instead of using reactor heat to expand large amounts of propellant through a nozzle, the nuclear plant operates in a closed cycle, using its thermal energy to produce large amounts of electrical energy. Electric rocket engines require only small amounts of propellant. In the ion rocket, for example, the working gas is ionized and electrostatically expelled (page 96). The ions have very small mass but very high velocities. In the plasma rocket the electrical current is fed into an arc which heats the working gas to partial ionization and the resulting plasma is accelerated electrodynamically.

Compared with the nuclear rocket developing perhaps 250,000 lb (113,400 kg.) thrust for 45 min. at the beginning of a flight to Mars, a large nuclear-electric system might produce as little as 20 lb (9·07 kg.) of thrust, but this could be maintained over very long periods including the time when more conventional rocket systems (chemical and nuclear) would be coasting on planetary trajectories without power. Depending on the availability of a suitable high power-to-weight ratio nuclear generator – at present the 'missing link' in projects of this kind – nuclear-electric drives may be expected, ultimately, to achieve much higher terminal velocities than either chemical or nuclear rockets.

When they become practicable, it should be possible both to reduce the launch weights of interplanetary vehicles and their mission times, and to travel much deeper into the Solar System.

As such vehicles will be incapable of launching themselves from the Earth, they must be assembled in parking orbits from modular components and stored in orbit near the destination and home planets. Once again this emphasizes the role of the future space station in performing assembly, fuelling, and maintenance tasks.

Hopefully, by the time such opportunities arise, the worst excesses of the space race will be over. An encouraging step has been the United Nations treaty on outer space, signed by the Soviet Union, the United States, and other countries, which provides for equal access to the Moon and other celestial bodies by all nations. From this could grow international collaboration in lunar exploration.

In establishing a scientific base on the Moon it would be folly not to employ the spacecraft of America and Russia in combined operations to ferry out prefabricated parts and keep the base supplied. Safety of the astronauts would be improved and so would the overall economics. The implications of a Lunar International Laboratory have been under study for several years within the Academy of Astronautics, established by the International Astronautical Federation, which draws upon the talents of distinguished scientists and engineers from East and West.

Similarly, there would be every advantage in organising manned interplanetary flight – particularly the exploration of Mars – as a combined operation.

In a climate of improving East-West relations following the end of the Vietnam War, it is not impossible that the Soviet Union would be prepared to join with the United States and other countries in planning joint expeditions. A small indication of progress was given by the Soviet scientist Professor Leonid Sedov at a recent congress of the International Astronautical Federation. 'A flight to Mars and the creation of large orbital stations, and other tremendous projects in space exploration,' he said, 'will certainly demand the joint efforts of all nations.'

Co-operation at the space frontier – with all its implications for improving living conditions on Earth, as well as pushing forward the boundaries of knowledge – would do much to unify technological effort on a broad front. Ultimately, this could benefit all mankind.

GLOSSARY OF SPACE TERMS

*These items refer to project studies only.

Ablation
erosion of a solid body (e.g. a spacecraft's heat shield) by a high-velocity, high-temperature gas stream

Ablative coating
thermal protection material applied to a re-entry body, which takes the brunt of aerodynamic heating

Abort
unscheduled intentional termination of a mission prior to its completion

Antipodal destination
a location on the opposite side of the globe from the point of departure; i.e. half-way around the Earth

Apogee
that point in a terrestrial orbit farthest from the Earth

Ballistic recovery (pure)
re-entry through the atmosphere along a free-fall path, without generating lift (similar to Mercury)

Ballistic recovery (semi)
partially lifting return to Earth, in a manner similar to the Apollo capsule which re-entered Earth's atmosphere from the Moon at 24,600 m.p.h. (39,600 km./hr.)

Ballute
a combined balloon/chute drag device deployed during early phases of re-entry for stability purposes

Beryllium
a heat-resistant structural material having a higher strength-to-weight ratio than aluminium

CG
centre of gravity, the point on a vehicle where all mass could be assumed to be concentrated

Closed loop
automatic control units linked together with a process to form an endless chain

CP   centre of pressure, the point on a surface where aerodynamic pressure distribution could be assumed to be concentrated

Cryogenics   the technology related to super-cold propellants such as liquid oxygen at $-297°$ F ($-183°$ C) and liquid hydrogen at $-423°$ F ($-252°$ C)

De-orbit   ejection from orbit by applying retro-thrust for velocity cancellation, prior to atmospheric penetration

Digital computer   a computer in which quantities are represented numerically and which can be used to solve complex problems

Electrolytical dissociation   separation of a chemical compound (such as water) into its elements (hydrogen and oxygen) by use of an electric current

EVA   extra-vehicular activity; man's operations outside a spacecraft, usually in orbit

Exponential increase   signifying a relationship factored by the power of a number, rather than a linear proportional growth

Force   that which moves an object from a state of rest, or produces a change in velocity (acceleration)

Guidance parameter a predetermined variable which is used to control a vehicle's flight path along a prescribed course or trajectory. Apollo guidance system controlled spacecraft's return to Earth from 193,000 miles (312,000 km.) when last midcourse correction was made

Heat flux   rate of thermal flow into a body, such as is encountered during return to Earth of Apollo from the Moon, when heat-shield temperature reached 5,000° F (2,760° C)

Hydrostatic buoyancy   the stable capability of an object to prevent oscillations, while floating on water (e.g. on the ocean surface)

*Hyperion   a rocket-vehicle concept for passenger transportation, which makes use of a catapult
launcher

ICBM   inter-continental ballistic missile; i.e. the pre-
decessors of today's space boosters

Isentropic   exhaust flow through a rocket nozzle, at no
expansion   change in internal thermal energy

*Ithacus   a rocket-vehicle concept for transportation of
military cargo or troops

Kinetic energy   energy contained by a body in motion, as
distinguished from potential energy due to the
body's altitude above the Earth's surface

Lifting body   a re-entry vehicle shape, with lift capability
somewhere between the semi-ballistic and
winged vehicles

L/D   the ratio of lift-to-drag when flying in an atmosphere, which is equal to the ratio of weight-to-
thrust during cruise

NASA   National Aeronautics and Space Administration

Orbital   speed of a body following a closed-loop trajectory,
velocity   generally applied to elliptical or near-circular
orbits; e.g. close to Earth at about 18,000 m.p.h.
(29,000 km./hr.)

Parabolic   speed of a body (following an open parabola
(escape)   trajectory) needed to escape from the gravitational field of a planet; e.g. departure from Earth
at about 25,000 m.p.h. (40,000 km./hr.)

Parabolic   a concrete dish shaped like an open conic sec-
reflector   tion, which will reflect all rays (emanating
from the focus point) in a direction parallel to
the longtitudinal axis of the parabola

Payload   that portion of a rocket's mass which is transfer-
(useful)   able at its orbital (or terrestrial) destination

*Pegasus   a rocket-vehicle concept for transportation of
commercial high-priority freight or passengers

*Project Deimos   a conceptual study which investigated the application of re-usable launch vehicles for a manned landing on Mars

*Project Selena   a conceptual study which investigated the application of re-usable launch vehicles for delivering cargo and personnel to the Moon for construction of a post-Apollo lunar laboratory

Quantum   implying a significant increase, usually tenfold (or an order of magnitude) improvement

Quasi-escape   close to escape velocity; e.g. about 6·95 miles/sec. (11·2 km./sec.), as related to the Earth's gravitational field

Re-entry corridor   the region where return to Earth is possible without skipping out of the atmosphere, and without burning up during re-entry; for Apollo's return from the Moon, this corridor was 30 miles (48·4 km.) wide

Retro-rocket   a rocket used for velocity cancellation; e.g. to return from orbit or to soft-land on Earth

*ROMBUS   re-usable orbital module-booster and utility shuttle; a rocket concept sized for delivery of about 1 million lb (454,000 kg.) of cargo to Earth orbit

Salvo-launched   a near-simultaneous dispatch of two or more rocket vehicles

*SARRA   Saturn application retrieval and rescue apparatus; similar to SASSTO, but with a payload compartment designed for orbital collection of inoperative satellites

*SASSTO   Saturn application single-stage-to-orbit; a re-usable high-performance S-IVB-sized stage used as a test-bed for booster recovery

Spaceport   an 'airport' of the future, where commercial rocket vehicles will take off, land, and be serviced for duty

Specific impulse	the thrust of a rocket in lb (or kg.) divided by its propellant consumption in lb/sec. (or kg./sec.) i.e., the time in seconds required for 1 lb of propellant to produce 1 lb of thrust
Stalling condition	whenever a vehicle in atmospheric flight loses sufficient horizontal velocity (and lift) that it begins to fall uncontrolled
Synchronous satellite	a spacecraft at such an altitude (22,300 miles or 35,800 km.) that its orbital period is 24 hr., i.e. it will keep pace with the Earth's rotation; hence, to an observer on Earth, it appears stationary.
Tank topping	keeping the tanks full (prior to launch) of cryogenic propellants which boil off under ambient temperature and pressure on Earth
Toroidal combustor	an unconventional design for a rocket combustion chamber, shaped like a hollow doughnut, and as large as the entire base diameter of a booster
Touch-down dispersions	miss distances associated with Earth-recovery impact point location from predicted spot; for Apollo's return from Moon this deviation was 2·84 miles (4·57 km.)
Trajectory	the curved path described by a vehicle in flight, under such forces as gravity, lift and/or drag
Truncated plug	a foreshortened cone-shaped nozzle for reducing engine weight during ascent, and for providing a blunt re-entry profile during recovery.
Ullage	The volume in a closed tank or container that is not occupied by the stored liquid; the ratio of this volume to the total volume of the tank; also an acceleration to force propellants into the engine pump intake lines before ignition
Vector	a force or velocity expressed as a line having a point of application, a direction, and a magnitude.

VTOHL   vertical take-off, horizontal landing; e.g. launched like a rocket and landed like an aeroplane

VTOVL   vertical take-off, vertical landing; e.g. launched like a rocket, and landed like a helicopter

INDEX

Numerals in **bold** refer to illustrations